A Primer on Folding Knives

by

Steven Roman
www.sroman.com

Copyright © 2015 by Steven Roman

Published by Innovative Textbooks

Contact: www.knifeprofessor.com
                   knives@knifeprofessor.com

Publication Date 07/22/2015

ISBN: 1-878015-31-1
ISBN13: 978-878015-31-0

Preface

This little book is designed for both new and experienced knife users who want to increase their knowledge of folding knives, affectionately known simply as **folders**.

Whether you want to buy just one or two folding knives, start an entire collection of these beautiful and strangely compelling tools, or already have a collection, making informed buying decisions, or just getting more satisfaction out of your current investment in knives takes a bit of knowledge about such things as knife terminology, knife anatomy and function, knife handle materials and especially the different types of steels used in knife blades. It is also important to have a basic understanding of knife sharpening techniques so you can maintain your knife collection in top working order.

There are literally thousands of folding knives on the market, ranging in price from under $40 for a surprisingly good-quality knife to over $25,000 (see Figure 1) and so making buying choices can be a bit bewildering. Hopefully, this book will help you make smarter buying decisions.

By the way, in case you need to make the argument to someone else (*ahem*), at least at the higher end, you can say that folding knives *are* less expensive than fixed-blade knives. For example, the **Gem of the Orient** fixed blade knife made by Nevada knife maker Buster Warenski sold for $2.1 million dollars, whereas the simple 7-inch (open length) William Henry Spearpoint 'Lace' knife pictured in Figure 1 sold for a mere $25,000. (Unfortunately, the William Henry knife it is out of stock at present☺.)

Figure 1: A simple $25,000 folder (William Henry Spearpoint 'Lace')

 # About Me

Since you paid good money for this little book, you have a right to know a little about me, the author. I will be brief. For more, please visit my web site at

www.sroman.com

I am a retired professor of (dare I say it) mathematics, having taught at a number of universities around the country over the past 40 years. After doing research for a number of years, I found that I enjoy writing books far more. I have written about 30 books in high-level mathematics (undergraduate, graduate and research level) and nine books in computer programming (Visual Basic, C#, Microsoft Access, Microsoft Excel and Microsoft Word).

I have also been a woodworker for more than 30 years. Here is one example of the type of furniture I like to make. This one took me about nine months to complete. The photography is not too good, but you get the idea.

Figure 2: A Newport blockfront—One of my efforts

Woodworking has given me a lot of experience working with cutting tools (chisels, planes, carving knives and so on). It has also given me a lot of experience *sharpening* cutting tools. Most of this experience relates to folding knives in one way or another.

I have been carrying and using folding knives for more years than I can remember. Finally, in retirement, I can devote some time to writing about knives.

Enough said. Thanks for taking up my book.

Contents

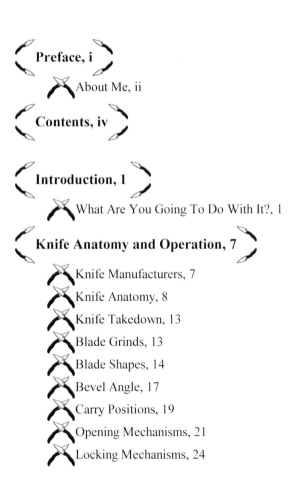

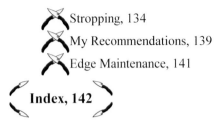

Introduction

What Are You Going To Do With It?

The first two steps in deciding what knife or knives to buy are probably deciding how much money you want to spend (at least initially) and deciding how you will be using your knives.

 Price Guidelines

Of course, budget decisions are strictly personal so I cannot really comment on them except to say that for many of us, this seems to be a moving target. Beware: knife collecting can easily become addicting!

However, I do want to set down some *rough* guidelines for those who are new to knife buying, as follows.

Down to Earth: Most Bang For Your Buck ($30–$50)

There are surprisingly many reasonably good quality knives in the $35–$50 price range, although it does take some effort to ferret them out. I would guess that the vast majority of these knives are made in China, but that does not *necessarily* mean that they are of poor quality. Indeed, I was told by the owner of one large knife company that by choosing manufacturing facilities carefully and maintaining strict supervision over production, it is possible to get high-quality products out of Chinese factories.

Although it is not my intention in this book to recommend specific knives, I will give you one example. I am quite impressed by the Spyderco Tenacious.

Figure 3: The Spyderco Tenacious

This Chinese-made knife is available on Amazon for about $35 (with a black G-10 handle). I own one and find its fit and finish to be excellent. The blade steel is quite functional, albeit not of the highest quality, which is to be expected for a knife in this price range. It is also one of the sharpest knives I have ever seen coming from any factory. (Of course, I may have just gotten lucky with my particular knife.)

The Troposphere: Most Bang For Your Buck Made in the U.S.A. ($50–$100)

In this price range, one can find many good quality knives made in the United States from a variety of knife manufacturers. This is the upper end of the knife price sweet spot, that is, the range in which you get the most bang for your buck, as they say.

The Stratosphere: High-Quality Production Knives ($100–$250)

I think that this is where you will find the "lower end" of the high-quality production knives that are made from high-end components. By high-end components, I mean blades made from the best steels, such as M390, ZDP-189, Elmax and S90V and handles made from high-end materials, such as carbon fiber. (I will discuss blade steels and handle materials in detail later in the book.)

The Mesosphere: Beginning Semi-Custom and Custom Knives ($250–$500)

This is the "higher end" of the high-quality production knives, along with some knives from smaller companies that are partly or completely handmade. The materials are generally high end and the additional labor put into the construction and assembly of the knives demands higher prices.

The Ionosphere: Very High-End Knives ($500–$1500)

Here we find some production knives, but mostly custom and semi-custom knives from smaller companies.

Outer Space: ($1500 and Up)

There are surprisingly many custom and semi-custom knives in this price range.

 # *Are They Worth The Price?*

Whether or not a knife in the higher price ranges, especially in the ionosphere and higher can possibly be worth the price is definitely in the eye of the beholder. I get a sense that there are really two types of really expensive knives. Some of these knives are hand made by companies or individuals who believe their knives are simply worth the price, based on the skill level required to manufacture the knife and the labor involved in that production. Or perhaps they just believe that the market will support their price points. I am not trying to pass judgment here—whether or not they are worth the price is ultimately up to the buyer and will certainly be a matter of opinion.

Other knives are highly priced because they are part knife–part jewelry, being adorned with precious metals such as gold or silver and precious gems, such as sapphires or diamonds. Many of these knives also involve a great many hours of engraving. If you are interested in watching a knife engraver at work, let me suggest the YouTube video

https://www.youtube.com/watch?v=L_H4ogdBBHo

At the higher price ranges, you are no longer paying for increased performance. For example, you can get a knife whose blade is made from a top-of-the-line steel like ZDP-189 for under 80 dollars. In fact, I think that for most people, the presence of precious metals or gems, or even just the presence of a high price tag, actually *decreases* usability. Would you use a $25,000 folder to cut up a bunch of cardboard boxes? How about a $5,000 folder? Or a $1500 folder? When you can finally say "yes" to this question, you will have determined where your price point is for a utilitarian knife.

So, your options are wide open. You can opt for just a single knife like the Spyderco Tenacious and spend a total of about $35. If you stop there and read this entire book, you will probably be the most well-informed person in the world who owns only one knife! At the other extreme, you can stock up on high-end, custom or semi-custom knives where the sky's not even the limit.

 Knife Usage

There are several ways in which we interact with knives.

Collecting

Many knife owners amass a substantial number of knives whose cutting edges never see action of any kind. I must admit to owning one or two such knives myself. I tell myself that I will use these knives, but they are so beautiful (and expensive) that I cannot quite bring myself to pull the trigger, so to speak. So I just take them out on a regular basis, open and close them several times, utter a contented sigh and put them away.

Of course, each person must decide for himself or herself what price point places a knife in the "don't use" category. In my fantasies, I would own at least two of every such knife so I could use one and stare at the other!

Investing

Some collectors lock the better part of their knife collection away in a safe and may even lose track of exactly what they own. Generally, these folks are hoping to sell some of their knives at a later date for a nice profit. In other words, they are *knife investors*.

Ordinary-use knives generally do not increase in value over time, but high-end knives can and often do increase in value. A **sprint run** is a production of a particular knife type that is based on a previous production but has upgraded features. Generally, the knife's blade will be made of a higher quality steel and the knife's handle will be made of a higher quality material. The knife may also have additional embellishments like gold anodized standoffs or handle inlays. A key point is that these productions are **limited run productions**, that is, only a limited number of such knives are produced. This can range from a single knife to 1500 knives, but it is *limited* and generally a *one-time* production.

These characteristics make a sprint run (or to a lesser extent any limited run production) highly collectable and it is *possible*, although by no means certain, that these knives will increase in value over time. Investors simply purchase such knives, put them away and offer them for sale at a later date and at a premium price in their *new, unused, unsharpened* condition. (eBay provides a readily accessible market for such knives.)

Just Plain Using

Most of us buy knives to use them, even if we are collectors or investors as well. Small, delicate knives with blades under about 3 inches in length, sometimes called **gentlemen's knives** are sufficient for light use, such as cutting string, small rope, paper, tape, the occasional cardboard box and most food.

For heavier use, such as cutting large boxes (cardboard is actually quite abrasive and therefore hard on a cutting edge), cutting heavy rope or cable ties and light wood carving, a larger knife is generally more appropriate.

If you want to take a knife with you while hiking or camping and expect to do some serious chopping or batoning of wood (pounding the knife blade through a piece of wood), you may want to consider a fixed-blade knife, since these are generally more substantial than folding knives. On the other hand, I have been in the presence of some very substantial folding knives that the manufacturers claim can do the work of a fixed knife, but I have not put this to the test.

 *EDC Knives*

You will encounter the term **EDC** quite often in your knife researches. EDC is an acronym for **Every Day Carry** and refers to knives suitable for carrying in your pocket on a daily basis, in both casual and formal attire. Of course, what constitutes an EDC is a matter of personal taste.

For my part, an EDC knife should be practical, relatively light, not too scary and perhaps even attractive. I sometimes worry about opening certain knives in, say a crowded restaurant because the knife might attract a few unwanted stares from neighboring tables. When I feel that way about a knife, I conclude that it is probably not a good EDC knife *for me*.

To illustrate, when I am dressed casually (which is most of the time), I carry a medium sized knife like the Zero Tolerance 0770CF. This exceptional knife has a 3.25 inch blade and weighs a light 3 ounces. (I generally don't care for assisted knives, but I do make exceptions, as in this case)

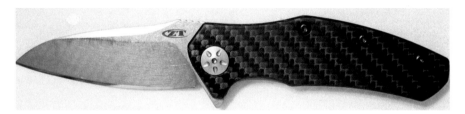

Figure 4: A medium-sized EDC knife (Zero Tolerance 0770CF)

For more dressy occasions, I might carry the beautiful William Henry knife in Figure 5. This knife has a 2.5 inch blade and weighs a mere 1.8 ounces. The bolster and lanyard beads are sterling silver, the scales are bone and the thumb stud is adorned with an opal.

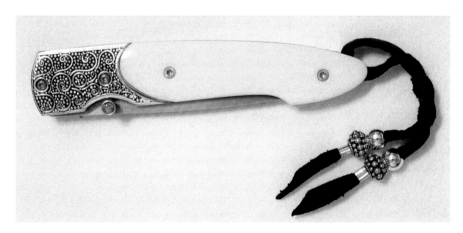

Figure 5: A small EDC knife (William Henry T-10 LE7)

On the other hand, I think that the knife in Figure 6, while very interesting, is a bit too fearsome for an EDC. It is also a bit too impractical for an EDC—I wouldn't want to try to trim a broken fingernail with this 9-inch knife!

Figure 6: The 9-inch Spyderco Civilian—Not my idea of an EDC knife

By the way, I know several knife users who like to carry *two* knives: a small razor-sharp knife for delicate cutting of things like food and a more substantial (and generally duller through use) knife for heavier cutting. There is probably no need to carry three knives … well, that is, unless you *want* to.

Knife Anatomy and Operation

 ## Knife Manufacturers

Knifes can be divided into three broad categories: **machine-made, semi-custom** and **custom** (or **hand-made**). A semi-custom knife is made partly by (often computer-aided) machine and partly by hand. Of course, the more labor that goes into a knife, the more costly the knife. But just because a knife is wholly or partly machine made does not in any way make the knife of lesser quality *per se*. There are many very fine knives of all types on the market.

On the other hand, I hope that at some point you get an opportunity to handle a fine custom-made knife. Perhaps your local knife store (if you have one) has some custom knives in stock. They can be a real treat to the eye and to the hand.

Those of you who are truly new to the knife world should at least see the names of some of the more prominent knife manufacturers. Here is a list in alphabetical order, with apologies to those manufacturers that I have not mentioned. (Custom knife makers are not included in this list.) As you can see, there is a lot to choose from.

Al Mar Knives	Guardian Tactical USA
Benchmade	Gerber
Böker	Ka-Bar
Buck Knives	Kershaw
Case Knives (W. R. Case & Sons)	Leatherman
Chris Reeve Knives	Mantis Knives
Cold Steel	Medford Knife and Tool
Columbia River (CRKT)	Microtech
Emerson	Ontario Knife Company

Protech	Strider Knives
Schatt & Morgan	Timberline Knives
Schrade	Victorinox
SOG	William Henry Studios
Spyderco	Zero Tolerance

Generally speaking, each knife company produces knives with a certain "personality." For example, there is *in general* no mistaking a Zero Tolerance knife with a Spyderco knife or a Buck knife or a Protech knife. As you become familiar with various brands of knives, you will probably get a sense of the differences between them as well as which personalities you prefer.

 # Knife Anatomy

Figure 7 shows the various parts of a folding knife in a side view and Figure 8 shows the various parts of a folding knife in a top-down view.

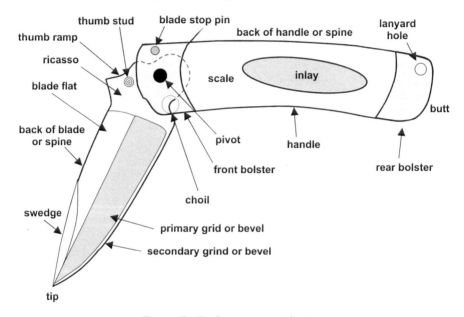

Figure 7: Knife anatomy–side view

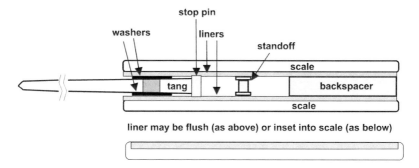

Figure 8: Knife anatomy–top view (no bolsters)

Let's go over some of these parts. You may wish to refer to the figures above.

 ## Handles and Bolsters

Each side of a knife handle may consist of a single part or multiple parts. A **bolster** is a metal portion of the handle that houses the **pivot pin**, around which the knife blade rotates. (The knife in Figure 5 has a sterling silver bolster.) However, if the handle material is strong enough, a separate bolster is not required and in this case a bolster becomes more of a design feature. Some knives have a rear bolster as well as a front bolster. The portion of the knife blade that lies within the handle is called the **tang** of the blade. The rotation of the blade is stopped by a **stop pin**, located where it will hit the tang of the blade once the blade reaches its fully open position.

 ## Knife Scales

The outside portions of the handle between the bolsters (if there are any) are called **scales**. (The knife in Figure 5 has scales made from bone.) Scales may contain a decorative or functional insert and they may also be lined with a metal liner, especially when extra strength is needed or to accommodate a liner lock (described later).

Knife scales are also an important *aesthetic* part of a knife, since they impart both feel and visual appearance to the knife. In fact, there is a thriving aftermarket business in custom scales for certain of the more popular production knives. For example, you may be able to replace the fiberglass scales on your favorite knife with carbon fiber or titanium or anodized aluminum scales, although the cost of custom scales may approach or even exceed the cost of the knife itself!

 ## Standoffs and Backspacers

The two sides of the handle are separated by **standoffs** and/or a **backspacer**. As mentioned earlier, standoffs are sometimes the target of custom modifications to a knife. For example, plain standoffs can be replaced by standoffs made of titanium or anodized aluminum.

Ricassos

Many knife blades have an exposed flat portion near the pivot. This is called the **ricasso**. Often, the ricasso, or the area of the blade where the ricasso would be if it were present, shows the manufacturer's logo, knife model number, blade steel type or other data.

Thumb Ramps with Jimping

Many knives have a **thumb ramp** on the spine of the blade near the heel. This ramp is designed for the user's thumb and is often jimped. **Jimping** is a series of striations cut in the metal that provide additional friction to help prevent a possibly wet thumb from slipping.

Choils

Many knife blades have a cutout portion directly opposite the thumb ramp. This cutout is called a **choil** and provides a place for the user's index finger. It is also often jimped. By placing the thumb on the thumb ramp and the index finger in the choil, the user can "choke up" on the knife for a firmer grip that lies closer to the cutting edge of the knife, thus increasing control over the blade.

Swedges

Some knives have a small ground-down portion in the spine of the blade, near the tip. This is called a **swedge** and is primarily for decorative purposes, although some might argue that a large swedge in a large knife will noticeably reduce the weight of the knife.

Primary and Secondary Grinds

If you scan the side of the blade from the spine to the cutting edge, you *may* first find a flat portion to the blade, called the **blade flat** (not to be confused with the ricasso, which is a flat portion at the *heel* of the blade only). Following the blade flat (if there is one), you will find a taper called the **primary grind** or **primary bevel** of the blade. At the very bottom of the blade lies the **cutting edge**, which is formed by a second very small taper or bevel, called the **secondary grind** or **secondary bevel**. Unfortunately, use of the terms primary and secondary differ. Some people refer to our primary bevel as the secondary bevel and vice-versa. I prefer to use the term **cutting bevel** since it unambiguously refers to the bevel that forms the cutting edge. The unqualified term "bevel" generally refers to the cutting bevel. (I will discuss *microbevels* in the chapter on sharpening.)

Washers and Ball Bearing Systems

Most folding knives use a pair of washers on either side of the blade tang to facilitate the rotation of the blade. In most cases, the washers are made of phosphor bronze or Teflon. Another technology that is used on some knives is **ball bearings**. There are two ball bearing systems commonly in use today.

In the **Ikoma Korth Bearing System** (**IKBS**™), loose balls are placed in a race (circular channel) cut directly into the titanium liners of the knife. For example, Figure 9 shows the IKBS system in a knife made by CRKT (Columbia River Knife and Tool).

Figure 9: The IKBS system in a CRKT knife (Courtesy of CRKT)

You can learn more about the IKBS system and even learn how to make it yourself at

http://www.ikbsknifetech.com/

The Kershaw knife company uses a technology they call **Kershaw Velocity Technology** or **KVT**. In this system, the balls are caged in a washer (see Figure 10) that is embedded in the liners of the knife.

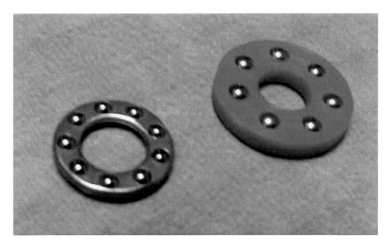

Figure 10: The KVT system by Kershaw (Courtesy of Kershaw)

It would seem that there are advantages and disadvantages to each system. As you can see from the pictures, on the one hand it seems that restraining the balls in a washer would provide more stability and make repairs to the knife much more pleasant by preventing the loss of balls if the knife needs to be disassembled. On the other hand, there are far fewer balls in the caged system, which implies that each ball will need to absorb more torsional force if the knife is used for such things as prying, for example.

Generally speaking, ball bearings are designed to operate at high speeds and under forces of considerable magnitude. However, knife blade rotation is relatively *very slow* and the forces are relatively *very weak* (unless of course you are fond of using your knife to pry boulders apart). Therefore, it might seem as though ball bearing systems should be superior to washers for knife construction. However, I do not believe that all the verdicts are in as yet and so we may need to wait some time before the advantages and disadvantage of ball bearing systems have been solidified.

One evident disadvantage of ball bearing systems is that unsealed ball bearing systems are particularly susceptibly to clogging with dirt and cleaning them is much more difficult than cleaning a washer.

Personally, I own one *custom* knife that is accoutered with ball bearings and the blade seems almost to *glide open by itself* once I tug gently on the flipper! It opens like none of my other knives. However, I also own another non custom, high-end ball-bearing knife that opens just like most of my other high-end washer-based knives. In fact, I didn't even know that it uses ball bearings until I read about it some time after I bought the knife.

I suspect that the reason that some ball-bearing knives don't feel any different than washer-based knives is that the momentum generated by the user in overcoming the force that holds the blade closed makes the blade fly open smoothly and quickly *in either case.*

In any case, more ball-bearing based knives will be appearing as time passes and only the passing of time will tell us whether or not they are the future of knife making.

 # Knife Takedown

In order to overhaul a knife or do a thorough cleaning and lubricating of a knife, or even to replace the scales on a knife, you will need to at least partially disassemble the knife. In knife parlance, disassembling a knife is called **takedown**. However, even though I do occasionally disassemble a knife, I cannot in good conscience recommend the process to others. Even mid-range production knives are assembled and *precision tuned* by hand and unless you are quite accomplished at tinkering with precision parts, you may never get the knife back to the same level of functionality as before it was disassembled. In fact, I have been told by the folks at one large knife company that fully 90% of the knives they receive from customers for "repair" arrive in the form of plastic bags full of loose parts! Enough said.

However, if you really want to disassemble a knife and are willing to accept the consequences, there are some caveats with which you should be aware. First, it will probably void your warrantee. Second, while some knives are easily disassembled and reassembled, others are not. For instance, the screws that hold the scales on may be secured *very tightly* using a substance called Loctite (or something similar) and you risk stripping the head of a screw, which is bad news indeed. Third, if you proceed, I recommend taking some pictures along the way. They may prove an invaluable reference when you attempt to reassemble your knife.

Finally, before disassembly, I would strongly suggest looking on YouTube to see if someone has already disassembled the same model knife on camera. This may prevent you from making an error in the takedown process.

 # Blade Grinds

Figure 11 shows the most common **blade grinds** in profile. Note that the pictures do *not* show the small cutting bevel—these profiles are for the *secondary* bevel.

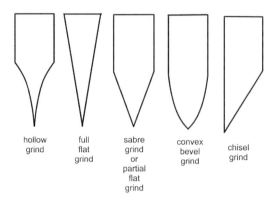

Figure 11: Some blade grinds

The concavity of a **hollow grind** may be pronounced or almost imperceptible. A hollow ground blade tends to have *slightly* better slicing performance that a flat grind (of the same thickness) because the primary bevel tends to be narrower and because friction is reduced somewhat by the concavity of the hollow grind. However, the cutting edge may also be weaker precisely because the blade is narrower.

Full flat grinds are quite popular, as are partial flat grinds, usually called **saber grinds**. **Convex grinds** arise when a knife is sharpened on a belt sander whose belt does not have a supporting platen and therefore flexes when the knife comes into contact with the belt. Convex grinds may also slightly reduce friction when slicing. Chisel grinds are not that common, but many Japanese knives are chisel ground, especially those intended for wood carving. **Marking knives**, which are used in woodworking to mark a straight line against a ruler are generally chisel ground, with both left and right hand versions available. (The flat side of the blade goes against the ruler and the bevel helps keep the knife against the ruler as you mark the line.)

As to the cutting (primary) bevel, I suspect that these bevels are generally so narrow that their geometry is not particularly significant to cutting performance. For example, I notice no difference in cutting performance when I sharpen a knife with the Work Sharp, which produces a convex cutting bevel as when I sharpen the same knife using a stone-based system, which produces a flat cutting bevel. (I have not tried sharpening my knives on a wheel-based system, which would produce a concave cutting profile.)

 ## Blade Shapes

Figure 12 shows some of the more common knife blade shapes. Among these, the **drop point** and **clip point** shapes are most common, followed by the **tanto**, **reverse tanto**, **spear point** and **sheepsfoot** shapes. Note that the spear point shape is quite similar to the drop point, but is symmetric.

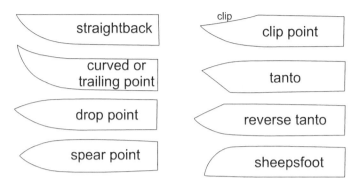

Figure 12: Common blade shapes

 The Belly of a Knife Blade

There does not seem to be a *clear and consistent* use of the term "belly" of a knife blade so let me suggest one here. As shown in Figure 13, the **belly** of a knife blade is that portion of the blade that lies below an imaginary straight line drawn from the tip of the blade to the bottom of the back of the *cutting portion* of the blade.

Figure 13: The belly of a knife

As you can see from Figure 13, a blade that has more curvature to the cutting edge, such as a drop point blade, has more belly, whereas a blade with no cutting-edge curvature, such as a sheepsfoot, has no belly at all.

 Recurve

Some knife blades have a concave portion at the head of the cutting edge, as shown in Figure 14. This is called a **recurve**.

Figure 14: A recurved blade (Kershaw Blur)

Some knife users find recurved blades to be more attractive, or at least more interesting than plain blades. Others find recurved blades to be simply an annoyance because a recurved blade can be harder to sharpen. A very subtle recurve does not seem to present too much difficulty, but a more pronounced recurve does require special sharpening techniques.

 Serrated Blades

Some folding knife blades are partially or even totally **serrated**, as shown in Figure 15.

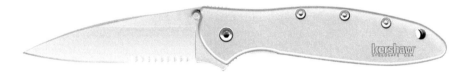

Figure 15: A partially serrated blade (Kershaw leek)

Generally speaking, there are two types of knife cutting actions: *slicing cuts* and *pushing cuts* (including chopping cuts).

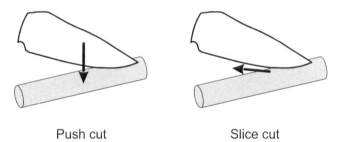

Push cut   Slice cut

Figure 16: Push and slice cuts

As shown in Figure 16, the difference between a push cut and a slice cut is in the direction of motion of the cutting edge with respect to the object being cut. In a **push cut**, the blade moves *perpendicularly* to the surface that is being cut. In a **slice cut**, the cutting edge moves at a non-perpendicular angle to the surface being cut.

The conventional wisdom is that **plain edges** (that is, non serrated edges) perform better when doing push cuts and give more control for accurate cutting. On the other hand, serrated edges perform better when slicing because the varying angles at which the cutting edge meets the object to be cut will allow the blade to grab the object and so a slicing motion with a serrated blade imparts more cutting force to the object.

Figure 17: The effect of a serration

More specifically, looking at Figure 17, as you move the knife back and forth over the rope, the cutting angle that the edge makes with the fibers of the rope is constantly changing and is often *perpendicular* to the direction that the knife is moving. In other words, slicing with a serrated edge is like performing a series of tiny pushing and pulling cuts *at different angles*, with considerable force.

It is also worth mentioning that a plain edge blade that is **toothy**, as shown in Figure 18, acts a bit like a serrated blade. This is why many experts say that a toothy edge is the best edge for kitchen knives, which do a lot of slicing.

MWwww\/Wwwww/Wwwww

Figure 18: A toothy edge

I should also mention that serrated edges present much more of a challenge to sharpen than plain edges. Flat stones cannot be used to sharpen the serrated portions of a blade. Instead, it is common to use a conical diamond or ceramic rod to hand-sharpen each serration separately. (The KME sharpener, which I will discuss in the chapter on sharpening does have a diamond cone accessory that allows you to sharpen the serrations of a blade with the same accuracy as you can with a plain edge.)

 # Bevel Angle

Figure 19 shows the **bevel angle** for a knife blade. This is the angle made by the *cutting* bevel and an imaginary plane containing the edge of the blade. Note the two commonly used angles: the **single-sided bevel angle** is exactly one-half of the **inclusive bevel angle**.

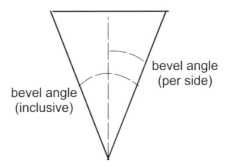

Figure 19: Bevel angle

There is much discussion concerning the best bevel angle for the cutting edge of a knife (or any cutting tool, for that matter). The most commonly suggested angles range from 14° per side to 22° per side. To illustrate the differences of opinion on bevel angle, Zero Tolerance knives are ground at 20-22 degrees per side and Spyderco knives are ground at 15-18 degrees per side.

The reason for this apparent disparity may lie in the fact that the appropriate bevel angle generally depends on two main factors: the type of steel used in the blade and how the knife will be used. For example, Zero Tolerance knives tend to be a bit more rugged than some other brands and so it may be anticipated that they will be used more aggressively, which begs for a wider bevel angle.

What I can say with certainty is that a smaller bevel angle makes for a more efficient, but weaker, cutting edge. This is fine for slicing tomatoes (or the occasional finger), but not for chopping logs in half. Thus, the optimal bevel angle depends on the intended use for the knife. It also depends on the steel used in the blade. Harder steels can hold an edge better at smaller bevel angles than softer steels, but they are also more brittle and so more prone to chipping at smaller bevel angles. Life is just not simple when it comes to bevel angles and you will need to experiment if you want to find the best bevel angle for your needs.

Of course, the alternative is to simply leave the factory angle, but you may find that an angle above 20 degrees is a bit too wide for general use. Changing the angle on a knife blade is called **reprofiling** the blade. Reprofiling a blade can take a bit of labor, especially with the new hard supersteels, because you may need to wear away a considerable amount of steel. You probably don't want to reprofile a knife more than once or twice.

While on the subject of reprofiling, here is a very valuable tip I got from Dan Dovel, the designer of the Work Sharp sharpening system. If the tip of one of your knives should break off and you decide to reprofile the knife to create a new tip, you should strongly consider grinding material from the *spine* of the blade to create the new tip, *not the cutting edge*. The reason is that if you take off too much material from the cutting edge of the blade, the location of the new tip may cause that tip to be exposed even when the knife is closed—a very dangerous situation! If you remove material from the spine of the blade, this danger is averted.

 # Carry Positions

Knives with pocket clips are designed to be carried *inside* the pocket with the clip on the outside.

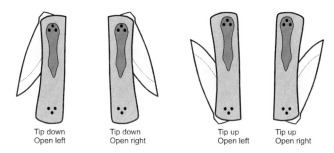

Tip down   Tip down   Tip up   Tip up
Open left   Open right   Open left   Open right

Figure 20: Knife carry positions in the pocket

As shown in Figure 20, if a knife's handle has appropriately placed screw holes, the knife can be carried **tip up** or **tip down** either with the opening to the left or to the right.

Some people feel that tip-up carry is more dangerous than tip-down carry because if the knife happens to be open when you reach into your pocket, you will likely get stabbed in the hand, a very nasty prospect indeed. Others feel that tip-down carry is more dangerous because if the knife opens in your pocket, it may stab you in the leg. This is certainly something you will need to decide for yourself. It may also be a bit safer to have the knife open towards the *side* of your leg rather than the front of your leg, where the more important parts reside, shall we say.

Another issue in considering whether to use tip-up or tip-down carry is the speed at which the knife can be brought "to the ready" after leaving your pocket. Many knife users like to **deploy**, that is, bring their knife to the ready position faster than a speeding bullet, as the saying goes. In fact, some knives are designed so that the seem of your pocket can open the knife as you remove it from your pocket! (I will discuss this in more detail a bit later.) Personally, I am quite happy to take a few seconds before I cut that piece of string or rope.

Pocket Clips

Pocket clips can be made of base metal or an upgraded material such as anodized aluminum or titanium and come in a variety of designs, some much stronger than others. The paint on less expensive pocket clips has a tendency to wear and can eventually look quite shabby. Anodized clips have a much more resilient finish. Also, there is a small cottage industry in aftermarket pocket clips for some knives. Custom pocket clips range from a few dollars to around $200!

As shown in Figure 21, a standard pocket clip (on the left) exposes a significant portion of the closed knife (say about 3/4 of an inch) above the top of the pocket.

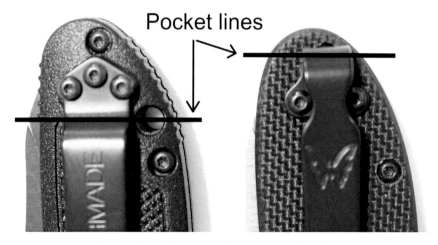

Figure 21: Standard and deep-carry pocket clips

Some find this exposure to be inappropriate for various reasons (too tempting to pickpockets, to visible to local authorities, etc.) or simply not fashionable. The **deep-carry pocket clip**, shown on the right in Figure 21, is designed to hide more of the knife from view. Some knives come with deep pocket clips. In other cases, the company may be willing to send you deep-pocket replacements at no cost.

Personally, I have mixed feelings about pocket clips. Since a pocket clip is designed to make it easier to access the knife by holding it high in your pocket, it must also be strong enough to keep the knife from falling out of your pocket. Unfortunately, this means that many pocket clips can be rather hard on the seem of your pocket. I value my EDP (every day pants) and don't want to see them ruined by knife pocket clips. One alternative is to carry your knife in a knife sheath on your belt. You can also carry a small knife loose in your pocket if that suits your needs.

Opening Mechanisms

Manual-Opening Knives

As shown in Figures 22, 23 and 24, most manual-opening knives use one of three common designs for easy opening: a **thumb hole** a **thumb stud** or a **flipper**. In the first two cases, to open the knife, the user places his or her thumb in the thumb hole or against the thumb stud (which is basically just a small post) and then rotates the blade in a direction *tangential* to the circle whose center is at the pivot and that passes through the thumb stud/hole. A flipper is operated by pulling it back with the index finger.

Figure 22: Thumb hole opening mechanism (Spyderco Gayle Bradley)

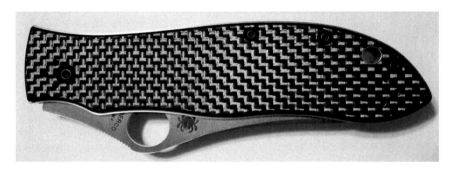

Figure 23: Thumb stud opening mechanism (Mel Pardue custom)

Figure 24: Flipper (and thumb stud) opening mechanism (Zero Tolerance 0562CF)

Thus, each of these opening methods is designed for **one-hand operation**. In practice, the ease with which a knife can be opened with only one hand depends to a large extent on how firmly the blade is held captive within the handle and also on the overall geometry of the knife. Some knives are simply more difficult to open with a single hand than others.

I have encountered a potential problem with thumb studs that is worth bringing to your attention. I once owned a knife with a thumb stud that was located a bit too far away from the handle of the knife, which left the stud a bit too exposed. On three separate occasions within a two-day period, the knife partially opened unintentionally when I tried to remove it from my pocket because the thumb stud got caught on my pant pocket seam. I no longer own that knife.

 Deployment Speed

While on the subject of knife opening, and as I mentioned earlier, some knife users like to deploy their knives with lightening speed. To this end, some Emerson knives employ the **wave shaped opening feature**, which is the hook at the top of the blade shown in Figure 25. (There are similar knives from other knife makers.)

Figure 25: The Emerson Wave hook (Emerson Super Commander)

This hook is designed to catch the edge of your pocket when you remove the knife and so by the time the knife has completely cleared your pocket, it will be fully opened! Figure 26 shows the action frozen at two points.

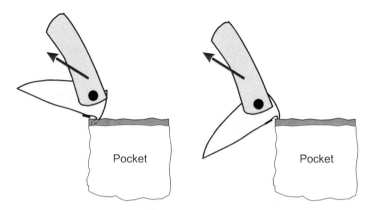

Figure 26: The Emerson wave feature

If you would like to see the wave feature in action, you might want to watch the following YouTube video

https://www.youtube.com/watch?v=AABt6c_MhfI

Note also another type of manual opening device on the blade in Figure 25. The small round disk in front of the wave hook functions just like a thumb stud. Personally, I find this mechanism to be rather awkward to operate, but that may be due simply to my weak fingers.

 Assisted Knives

Assisted knives have a spring that snaps the blade open once the user begins the opening process. Assisted knives generally have a thumb stud or a flipper. Many knife enthusiasts like assisted knives but many do not. I suppose that many people are concerned that the knife will fly open in their pocket. Some (but not all) assisted knives have additional locking mechanisms to prevent accidental opening, but this defeats one of the main purposes of assistedness, namely, rapid deployment. Oh well, better safe than rapid, I guess.

It is often possible to **deassist** an assisted knife by partially disassembling the knife and removing the spring. I have done this myself on several knives. The same takedown caveats apply here, with one addition. After the spring is removed from an assisted knife, the issue arises as to whether the blade will remain *securely* encased in the handle. If the main force keeping the blade in the handle was the assist spring, then there could be a problem. However, if the detent is strong enough to keep the blade retracted, all will be well. (I will discuss detents later.) This can only be determined by deassisting the knife or by checking with someone who has deassisted the same model knife. Once again, before deassisting a knife, it might be worth checking on YouTube to see if someone has already done this on camera.

Automatic Knives

Automatic knives open with the push of a button and were once called **switch blade knives**. There are strict laws concerning automatic knives in most states, so be forewarned. In fact, it might be a good idea to check both your state *and local* laws concerning carrying knives of *any* type. There may be blade length limits in your area. Also, carrying a knife hidden in your pocket may be considered carrying a *concealed weapon*, whereas carrying a knife in your pocket partly exposed using a pocket clip may be perfectly fine. Good luck on this.

Actually, in some parts of the country, automatic knives are legal if and only if the blade length is under 2 inches. The California-based knife company Pro-Tech produces some automatic knives just for this market. Figure 27 shows the Half Breed from Pro-Tech, a very well made little switch blade for the kid in most of us.

Figure 27: The Half Breed automatic knife (Pro-Tech)

Locking Mechanisms

Not all folding knives have locking mechanisms. After all, normal cutting and slicing actions act to keep the blade open and so, for these purposes, no locking mechanism is needed. That notwithstanding, there are a variety of locking mechanisms for knife blades, the most common of which are as follows.

LockBack Locks

The **lockback lock** is shown in Figures 28, 29 and 30.

Figure 28: Lockback lock—blade partially open

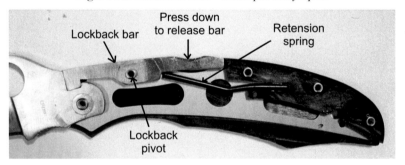

Figure 29: Lockback lock—blade open

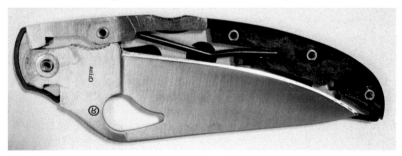

Figure 30: Lockback lock—blade closed

When you press down on the **lockback bar**, which is a substantial metal bar running along the spine of the handle, the bar rotates around the **lockback pivot** so that the front of the bar raises up and releases the blade. The lockback bar is held in the locked position by the **retention spring**. Note that the lockback bar is also responsible for holding (but not locking) the blade in its closed position.

Personally, I find lockback locks to be somewhat less ergonomic than other locking mechanisms. In fact, I once bought a knife that I liked *very* much—Its small size and elegant design approached perfection for me. However, perhaps precisely because the knife is small, my thumb was so close to the lockback pivot that the force required to disengage the lock was beyond my comfort level. (There is also no cutout for the thumb and the edges of the lockback bar are a bit sharp, which I believe to be a design flaw.) I realized reluctantly that this knife was not for me.

I should also mention that lockback knives require some special attention when closing, lest you cut yourself. (This really applies to all types of knives, but I think more so to lockback knives.) Specifically, if you hold the knife as in Figure 31 when you disengage the lock, the blade may very well swing down and back up into your finger, causing a nasty cut! (This happened to me *twice* when I got my first lockback knife many years ago. You would think that I would have learned after the first time!)

Figure 31: The WRONG way to close a lockback knife with one hand

Figure 32 shows the correct way to perform a one-handed closing of a lockback knife. By placing your index finger close enough to the pivot point of the knife, you can prevent the cutting edge of the blade from contacting your finger. (Of course, you can always use your other hand to control the blade movement.)

Figure 32: The correct way to close a lockback knife with one hand

 *Liner Locks*

Figures 33 and 34 show the **liner lock**.

Figure 33: The liner lock

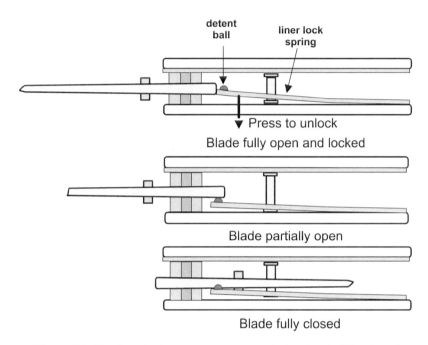

Figure 34: The liner lock top view: open, partially closed, fully closed

In a liner lock, the lower liner has a cutout that is bent up into the knife and acts as a spring. When the blade is in the fully open position, the liner lock spring snaps to its highest position and its end rests tightly against a *flat spot* in the tang of the blade, thus locking the blade open.

To disengage the lock, you just push the spring out of the way (towards the scale) with your thumb through a crescent-shaped cutout in the handle's scales. As the blade rotates towards the closed position, the liner spring's **detent ball** is the only contact point between the liner spring and the blade tang and so there is very little friction between these parts, making for a very smooth motion as the blade rotates closed. Finally, in the closed position, the detent ball falls into a **detent** (hole or dimple in the tang), thus holding (but not locking) the blade in the closed position.

Of course, the strength with which the blade is held in the closed position, and therefore the amount of force required to open the blade depends on the size of the detent and detent ball as well as the strength of the liner lock.

 Frame Locks

As shown in Figure 35, frame locks work in precisely the same manner as liner locks, except that they do not use a liner.

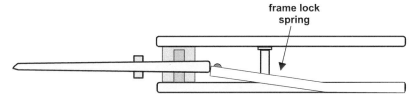

Figure 35: The frame lock

Figure 36 shows a knife with a frame lock.

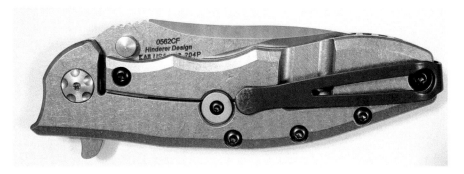

Figure 36: Frame lock (Zero Tolerance 0562CF)

Instead, the scales themselves are sufficiently strong (titanium alloy for example) that the cutout for the spring can actually be made in the lower scale.

Frame lock knives may be a little stronger than liner locks by virtue of the fact that a frame is thicker than a liner. However, the difference is probably not significant under normal knife use. One thing to keep in mind about frame locks is that the two sides of the knife do not have the same appearance because of the cutout on one side. If you are into symmetry, you may dislike the looks of a frame lock. For example, Figures 24 and 36 show the two sides of the same knife.

 Compression Locks

Figure 37 shows the **compression lock**, which works on the same principal as the liner lock, but the lock spring is cut out of the liner at the spine of the handle. Compression locks are not nearly as common as liner locks. While I like compression locks, I have found some of these locks to be quite sticky, much more so than liner locks and so I would advise caution when purchasing a knife with a compression lock. If you cannot try out the lock before buying, at least make sure you can return the knife if it is not to your satisfaction.

Figure 37: The compression lock

 Axis-Like Locks

The Benchmade knife company uses a lock on many of their knives that they call the **Axis**® **lock**. Some other knife manufacturers have a similar style lock. The Axis lock is shown in Figures 38–41.

Figure 38: The Axis lock

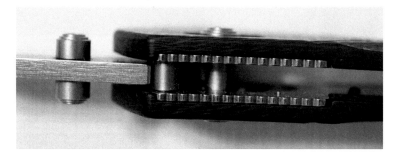

Figure 39: The Axis lock from the top

Figure 40: The Axis lock—internal view showing retaining spring

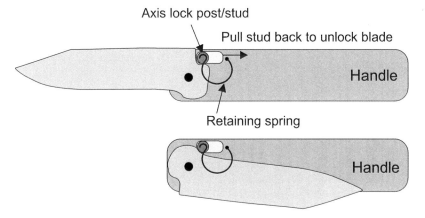

Figure 41: Axis lock mechanism

The Axis lock (and similar locks from other knife makers) has a post that protrudes out through both sides of the handle and rests in a rectangular cutout in the scales. The post is under spring tension that tends to push it towards the blade-side of the handle. Figure 40 shows that the spring is actually on the outside of the liner. However, to get an idea of how the Axis lock works, Figure 41 shows the parts with the liner removed.

As you can see, when the blade is fully open, the post is held tightly above a *flat* portion of the tang, thus preventing the blade from rotating. If the user pulls the Axis post back using thumb and forefinger (one on each side of the handle), the post moves back and out of the way and the blade is free to rotate. Once closed, the Axis post springs forward again to hold (but not lock) the blade closed. Indeed, operating the thumb stud provides sufficient force to pull the Axis stud back and allow the blade to rotate to the open position.

 *Button Locks*

The button lock is shown in Figure 42.

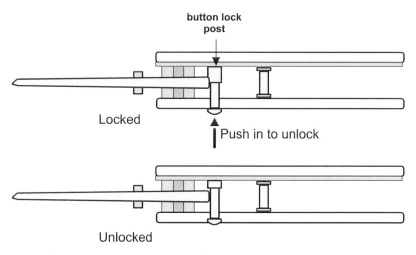

Figure 42: The button lock

In the locked position, the button lock post's thick portion is engaged within a cutout in the blade's tang. When the user pushes the button, the thicker portion is moved out of the path of the blade and the blade can rotate. Once the blade is closed, the thicker portion of the post holds the blade closed.

Figure 43 shows a special edition William Henry button-lock knife. The button lies in the center of a flower and is adorned with a blue sapphire. (The pivot also lies in the center of a flower.) The bolster and lanyard beads are sterling silver, the gemstones are sapphires and the scales are desert ironwood. The blade is DLC-coated ZDP-189. Only 25 of these beautiful knives were made during May and June of 2008.

Figure 43: A button lock (William Henry B-15 Prospector)

 *My Preferences*

Let me take an author's prerogative and give you my personal opinion about these locks. My preferences (which may *easily* differ from yours) are as follows:

1) Axis lock. This is my favorite lock because I find it extremely easy to operate. The Axis stud is just in the perfect position for me. The lock is designed to be worked using *both* the thumb and index finger. A very smoothly working Axis lock can be worked by pulling back on only one side of the Axis stud, but I suspect that this might cause some undesirable wear over time. (Unfortunately, Benchmade was the *only* company to ignore my repeated attempts to speak with someone in the company, so I can't verify this fact with them directly.)

2) Compression lock. A *properly working* compression lock, that is. As with the Axis lock, I find that my fingers can easily reach the lock and if it is working smoothly, I have no trouble disengaging it.

3) Button lock. When a button is large enough to be comfortable and located properly, I find this lock to be very easy to use. However, I have (rarely) encountered buttons that are so small and pointed as to be very uncomfortable, cutting into my finger as I press down.

4) Liner lock. Generally, I like this lock. Rarely, I find a liner lock to be either a bit too stiff or a bit too awkward for easy access. For example, some knives do not have a cutout for access to the liner lock and so it is necessary to *dig in* a bit with your thumbnail in order to operate the lock. I find this to be awkward at best. Also, when operating a liner lock, your fingers are in the path of the blade as it is closing and so some extra caution is required. However, I do not mean to imply that this is really a problem.

5) Frame lock. As to functionality, I have the same feeling about the frame lock as the liner lock, but aesthetically, I do not care for the frame lock. However, I do

own two frame lock knifes because I like the knives well enough to overlook the asymmetric look, so the lock is not a deal breaker for me.

6)   Lockback. Although a very good lock, I find it to be the least comfortable for my hands. Still, I do own a couple of lockback knives.

 Slip-Joint Knives

As I mentioned earlier, not all folding knives have locking mechanisms. The most common form of non locking knife is the **slip-joint knife**, an example of which is shown in Figure 44.

Figure 44: A slip-joint knife (Boker Stockman)

The blade of a slip-joint knife is held in either the open or closed position by a simple spring. For a nice description of some of the various types of slip-joint knives, I recommend the following link

http://www.knife-depot.com/knife-information-157.html

 Blade Lock Issues

Lock issues revolve around the properties of lock strength, lock reliability, lock ergonomics and possible design flaws.

 Lock Strength

Lock strength is the ability of a *properly functioning* lock to hold the blade in the open position under *appropriate* stress (for example, cutting, stabbing or light prying).

There is considerable Web traffic on the subject of which locking mechanisms are the strongest. While much of this speculation is probably only of academic interest, some of it has a sound basis for concern. When a knife is in the open position, the main concern is whether it might accidentally close while your fingers are wrapped around the handle—a very unpleasant prospect indeed. Of course, cutting and slicing cannot lead to this possibility. On the other hand, stabbing might because the stabbing motion, if done incorrectly, can exert a *closing* rotational force on the knife, as shown in Figure 45. The stabbing force should be directed from the blade tip to somewhere *above* the pivot.

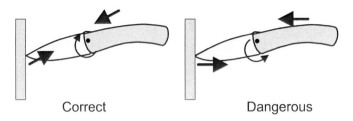

Correct   Dangerous

Figure 45: Stabbing forces on a knife

Fortunately, it seems that today's lock designs are sufficiently strong to hold the blade in place during *appropriate* knife usage, that is, provided that the lock is *fully engaged and working as designed.*

 Lock Reliability

A lock may be more than adequately strong but this is useless if the lock does not engage properly. **Lock reliability** is the ability of the lock to function as designed *every time* it is employed. Even one failure in a hundred thousand is way too many for my taste!

As an example of lock reliability (or lack thereof), I once purchased a liner lock knife whose lock barely extended enough to engage the blade tang. Figure 46 shows a properly engaged liner lock (the top figure) and a precariously engaged liner lock (the bottom figure). The lock *did* hold the blade securely closed for the short time that I owned the knife, but it's reliability certainly had me worried, so I returned the knife to the place of purchase with an explanation of the issue.

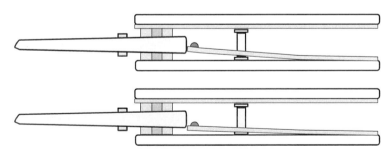

Figure 46: A poorly engaged liner lock (bottom figure)

Lock Ergonomics

Lock ergonomics is the ease with which a properly functioning lock can be engaged and disengaged by the user. Unlike lock strength and lock reliability, lock ergonomics is generally a matter of personal preference. For example, some user's find lockback locks awkward to operate; others do not.

Personally, I have experienced several knives with sticky locks. In some cases, the knife just needed a breaking in period. After opening and closing the knife a few hundred times, the lock operated properly so I put a positive spin on this by chalking it up to exceptionally fine manufacturing tolerances. However, some knives did not succumb to this breaking-in ritual. I remember one *very* expensive knife with a sticky lock that did loosen up after some six or seven hundred closings.

Design Flaws

An issue that stems from a possible design flaw is whether or not a lock is prone to *accidental* release by the user's hands. Yet another possible issue is whether a lock is prone to fail due to a propensity to collect dirt (such as the ever-present pocket lint) in the wrong places. In any case, it is worth keeping your knives clean to avoid any possible problems in this regard.

Handle Materials

Many knife handles are made from well-known materials such as aluminum, titanium alloy, bone or wood-metal combinations. Knife handles are also made from the following less familiar materials.

G-10

G-10 is formed from layers of fiberglass cloth that are soaked in a resin, then compressed and baked. Figure 47 shows an example of a textured G10 handle.

Figure 47: Textured G10 handle (Spyderco Para Military 2)

G-10 is very hard, very lightweight and dimensionally stable. It is often checkered or dimpled to reduce slipping and colored for aesthetic purposes. G-10 is used extensively in the electronics industry because it is an excellent electrical insulator.

By the way, the G-10 on most low to mid-range production knives may not be the most attractive, but I have a custom knife with smooth-as-silk polished G-10 scales, so I know that G-10 has great *potential* as a high-end handle material.

Figure 48: Polished G10 (Chamblin custom knife)

 ## Fiberglass Reinforced Nylon (FRN)

Fiberglass reinforced nylon (FRN) is a nylon-based plastic that is reinforced with glass fiber and then injection molded. FRN is very tough and more flexible than G-10. It is also often patterned (checkered or scaled, for example) and colored. FRN is also used in cooking utensils. Figure 49 shows a scaled FRN handle.

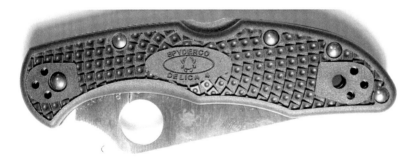

Figure 49: FRN handle (Spyderco Delica)

 ## Micarta

Micarta is a brand name of Norplex-Micarta and is a molded product "combining paper, cotton, and glass fabric substrates with phenolic resin, epoxy resin, or melamine resin." It is widely used in electrical and mechanical devices and also in military applications. Micarta is moderately hard, smooth, lightweight and strong. You can even find recipes on the Web for homemade Micarta in case you want to make your own handles! The term *Micarta* is often used generically (and incorrectly) for general phenolic laminates. Micarta handles, especially in the hands of custom knife makes, can be stunning in my opinion. Figure 50 shows a Micarta knife handle.

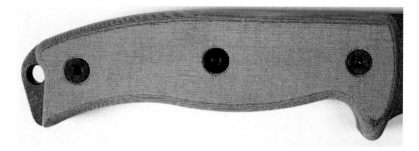

Figure 50: Linen Micarta handle (Esee 6 fixed-blade knife)

 *Carbon Fiber (CF)*

Carbon fiber (often abbreviated **CF**) consists of thin strands of (mostly pure) carbon tightly woven into a pattern and set in an epoxy resin, as shown in Figure 51.

Figure 51: Carbon fiber handle (Spyderco Caly 3.5)

Carbon fiber is one of the hardest of the knife handle materials. Carbon fiber may be stronger than both G-10 and FRN but it is also somewhat more brittle. It is also very lightweight and rather expensive, which is why carbon fiber knives tend to cost more than G-10 or FRN knives. Personally, carbon fiber is my favorite knife handle material.

Blade Construction

Most knife blades are made from solid steel. However, as shown in Figure 52, some knife blades have a **laminate** design, where the **core** of the blade is made from a hard steel that gives superior edge performance (but is more brittle) and the **outer steel** is a softer steel that is tougher (less brittle) and may also have better corrosion resistance.

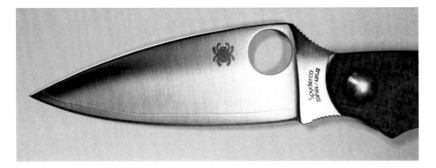

Figure 52: A laminate blade (Spyderco Caly 3.5)

For example, the knife shown in Figure 52 has a very hard ZDP-189 steel core and a softer, less expensive but highly corrosion resistant 420J2 steel outer layer. You can see the demarcation line about 3 millimeters above the cutting edge.

 ## *Damascus Steel*

A **Damascus blade** is made from several layers of different types of steel that are repeatedly folded and forged to produce a complex pattern on the surface of the blade, as shown in Figure 53. Damascus steel has been used in Indian, Chinese and Middle Eastern sword making.

Figure 53: A damascene pattern blade (William Henry)

Production of true Damascus steel gradually declined and stopped entirely sometime in the 18th century, after which the original Damascus production technique appears to have been lost. Today's techniques for producing Damascus-like steel are generally referred to as **pattern-welding**.

Pattern-welded blades can be quite striking in appearance (as in Figure 53) but their utility is a question that is open to debate. One potential issue is that these blades are so attractive and expensive that you may not want to risk using them. That aside, the usability of a Damascus blade must surely depend upon the steels used in making the blade as well as the technique for making the blade.

In case you are interested in the origin of the word "Damascus," it appears that during the time of the Crusades (say in the 11th and 12th centuries), Christian warriors discovered, probably much to their regret, that the Moslems possessed swords whose steel was superior to their own. It seems that these superior swords were encountered by the Christians in the city of Damascus, Syria. Apparently, these "Damascus" swords were forged directly from small ingots of steel formed in crucibles and given the name **wootz steel** by English-speaking people much later (in the 18th century). It has been shown that Damascus steel first appeared around the second century AD and was produced in India, the Middle East and China.

The crucible-made steel of Damascus swords is a surprisingly clean steel with a carbon content in the range of 1.1% to 1.8% by weight. Most modern knife steels have a carbon content in the range of roughly 0.7% to 1.5% but the top-quality knife supersteels have a carbon content in the range of 1.4% to 3.0%.

The beautiful patterns that often occur on Damascus blades actually appear only on the better quality blades and are referred to as a **damascence pattern**. It is probably because well made modern pattern-welded swords have similar patterns that the term "Damascus" is often applied to these modern blades as well.

Blade Coatings

Blades can be **coated** to reduce the effects of friction or to provide additional corrosion and wear resistance. Also, military and law enforcement agencies often prefer coated blades because they reduce or essentially eliminate glare. Here are some common blade coatings. There is debate as to which coating is the most wear resistant, but DLC and B4C may be the hardest coatings.

- **Black Electroplating (BLP)**: A coating adhered to steel using an electrostatic process.
- **Diamond-Like Coating (DLC)**: An amorphous carbon material that displays some of the properties of diamond. Also called **PVD**, which stands for **Physical Vapor Deposition**.

- **Titanium CarboNitride Coating (TiCN)**: A very hard titanium nitride coating. Also used as a non-toxic coating for medical implants.
- **Boron carbide coating (B4C)**: B4C (the actual chemical formula for boron carbide is B_4C) is an extremely hard boron-carbon ceramic coating. As a side benefit, B4C can absorb neutrons without forming long-lived radioisotopes and so forms an excellent absorbent for neutron radiation arising in nuclear power plants. This alone should be reason enough to convince your wife (or husband) that you should buy that B4C coated blade, right?

Figure 54 shows two knives with DLC blades. The top knife is a Spyderco Para Military 2 with a plain DLC. The bottom knife is a special William Henry knife model T12-BT (named the **Black and Tan**) that has a highly polished DLC, as you can see by the reflection of the pen tip in the blade.

Figure 54: Knives with DLC—Spyderco Para Military 2 and William Henry T12-BT

 # Blade Finishes

A **blade finish** is a surface treatment applied to the blade. Speaking in general terms, there are three types of blade finishes: polished, dull (also called **satin**) and very dull. Polished blades have a mirror-like finish, such as the William Henry knife in Figure 54. Polishing smoothes the surface of the blade, which helps to prevent corrosion.

However, polished blades show scratch marks more readily than the other finishes, some of which are purposely designed to hide untoward marks.

At the other extreme, for tactical purposes, law enforcement and military officials generally prefer a non-reflective (very dull) blade, since it will not do at all to have your knife blade glare at the enemy! However, the little nooks and crannies in the blade will trap moisture and so these blades are more prone to corrosion than other types of blades.

Most knives fall into the dull category—the blade that is, not the knife. These knives show the grinding marks and are dull because they are neither deliberately polished nor deliberately made very dull.

Figure 55 shows a few of the more common non-mirror blade finishes.

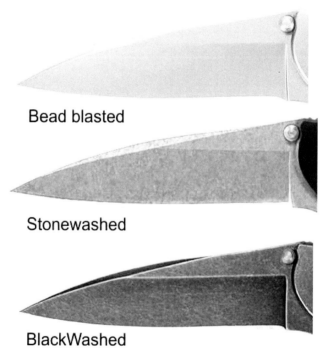

Bead blasted

Stonewashed

BlackWashed

Figure 55: Some blade finishes

Bead blast finish is a non-reflective finish applied to the surface by bead blasting or sand blasting the blade. This finish is also commonly referred to as a **military finish**. A **stonewashed finish** is applied by tumbling the blade together with an abrasive material. This leaves an "even but random" (a definite oxymoron) scratch pattern that tends to mask scratches that may occur with use.

Here is what Kershaw says about their **BlackWash finish** "[it] gives a knife that already-broken-in look—like a favorite well-worn pair of jeans. The coating provides an extra measure of protection for the metal, and the BlackWash helps hide any additional scratches you may put on the knife during normal use."

Scotchbrite finishes are also popular, since they blend the grinding marks on the blade, leaving a brushed appearance.

Figure 56 shows micrographs of some blade finishes. Note that the bead blast finish is quite uniform, unlike the stonewashed finish. The belt grind finish is the finish left on "unfinished" knives. Note also the smoothness of the polished DLC finish of the William Henry knife pictured in Figure 54.

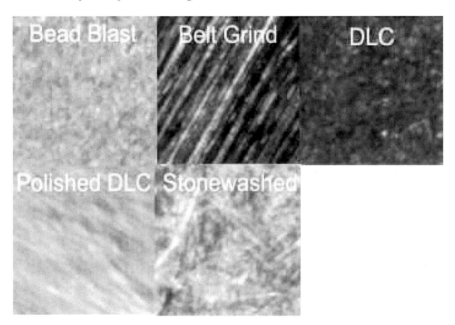

Figure 56: Micrographs of some blade finishes (45x)

 # Knife Care

If you have invested in some high-quality knives, you will certainly want to protect your investment. Fortunately, knife care is very straightforward.

 *Blade Care*

If a knife blade is caked with an undesirable substance, such as dirt, wood sap or glue from tape, it should be cleaned as soon as possible *and before closing the knife if practical.* Hot water and a mild dishwashing soap may be sufficient. If not, a biodegradable citrus-like cleaner may do the trick. Glue-like substances can be removed using a safe solvent like Goo Gone.

Whatever you use, it is probably a good idea to wash the blade with mild soap and hot water afterward and then *dry it thoroughly.* Compressed air is a big help in drying the internal parts of a knife, which are likely to get wet even if you are only washing the blade. If compressed air is not available, then blow gently (try not to spit) into the knife and let it air dry.

Even stainless steel can rust. Whatever kind of steel is used in a knife, some care should be taken to protect the blade from rust. There are many products on the market that impart corrosion resistance. For many years, I have used jojoba oil or camellia oil on my knifes and woodworking tools with great success. These oils also protect wood as well as metal. Use them *very sparingly.*

Sentry Solutions makes a number of cleaning/lubricating products, including a product called **Tuf-Glide**, which can be applied as a liquid or by using an impregnated cloth called **Tuf-Cloth**. Be aware, however that Tuf-Glide has a "distinct and strong" odor, which the company says will dissipate with time.

Scratches on DLC

Let me tell you a brief story about scratches in DLC (diamond like coating). I bought a very expensive knife that was completely DLC coated, blade and handle. This is a beautiful knife! However, the knife had a copper-colored scratch in the handle. I called the company, but they said there was nothing they could do to remove the scratch.

However, realizing that DLC is *very* hard, it occurred to me that whatever scratched this knife probably didn't actually scratch off any DLC, but rather left some of itself on top of the DLC. So I took out a Ballistol wipe that I had bought on Amazon, rubbed the scratch a bit, vigorously brushed the Ballistol into the handle with a firm toothbrush and left the cloth on the scratch. Then I placed a small piece of wood over the cloth and carefully clamped the "Ballistol/knife sandwich" together, with only *light* pressure. (For those who are not familiar with Ballistol, it is an eco-friendly cleaner, protector and lubricator that can be used on metal, leather and other materials.)

The next day, the "scratch" was gone. I hope that helps you some day.

Lubrication

Some folding knives will require lubrication from time to time. There are exceptions, however, and you should check with the company on this issue.

To lubricate the pivot area of a folding knife, you can use an oil lubricant or a dry lubricant such as a teflon-based lubricant. Both types of lubricants go on wet, but the dry lubricants will dry (hence the name). Whichever you use, use it sparingly! A single drop may be plenty, especially if you immediately work the knife by rotating the blade a few times. If the applicator bottle does not have a nice spout, you can invest is a small plastic bottle with a metal needle-like applicator for very precise application. They cost only a few dollars on Amazon.

 Thorough Cleaning

If your knife is in serious trouble, for example, if rotating the blade produces a *grinding* sound and simple lubrication does not resolve the problem, then you may need to do a more stringent cleaning, that is, you may need to disassemble the knife, clean each part separately, reapply grease to the pivot area (washers and posts) and reassemble. Fluorinated grease works well for this. For reasons outlined earlier, I do not recommend disassembly unless you feel that it is *absolutely necessary* and unless you are willing to accept the risk. (Remember the plastic bags full of knife parts.) A good alternative is to send the knife back to the manufacturer for servicing.

 # Exotic Folders

I want to conclude this chapter with a look at a few of the more exotic folders available.

 The Karambit

Figure 57 shows a modern **karambit** (or **kerambit**). This knife probably originated in Southeast Asia around the 11th century and was probably inspired by a cat's claw; that is, a *big* cat's claw!

Figure 57: Modern karambit (Mantis Knives MK3VBX)

Originally, the karambit was used as an agricultural tool, for things like planting and cutting roots. It is also quite effective for ripping open large sacks of grain. Later, as you might imagine, the karambit developed into a formidable weapon.

The karambit is designed to be held with the blade pointing *down*, either facing inward or outward and with the *index* finger through the large ring at the base of the handle. This makes it very difficult for an opponent to disarm a person holding the knife.

 The Balisong

Figure 58 shows a **balisong**, also known as a **butterfly knife**, which originated in the Batangas province of the Philippines. The two-piece handle separates and rotates to enclose the blade.

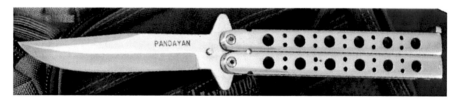

Figure 58: A balisong knife (www.balisong.com)

The balisong is a formidable weapon in the hands of an experienced user, who can manipulate the knife in an astounding variety of ways—all faster than the eye can see.

Indeed, it is impossible to do justice to the use of a balisong with a static medium like this book. If you are at all curious, I suggest you search for the word balisong on YouTube. Some of the instructional videos are quite remarkable.

Also, you may want to visit

www.balisong.com

which is purportedly "the home of the original Balisong, occasionally called the Batangas knife, a deadly weapon that, in the hand of an expert, can be opened as fast as, if not faster, than a Western switch blade."

The balisong is illegal in several states in the Unites States as well as in many other countries. (However, you can buy a balisong trainer, which as a non offensive "blade" on Amazon.) After you have watched a few of the balisong videos, you will understand why.

Incidentally, Mantis Knives makes the karambit/balisong crossover knife shown in Figure 59. Now you can have a bit of each world in one knife. According to the owner of the company, this knife is so popular that the company now makes it in other colors!

Figure 59: A karambit/balisong crossover (Mantis Knives MK-4)

Steel Metallurgy in Brief

(*I am indebted to Professor John D. Verhoeven, whose book* Steel Metallurgy for the Non-Metallurgist *served as a valuable aid to me in writing this chapter. I would also like to thank James Beckman, President of Crucible Industries® for taking the time to consult with me on the subject of steel metallurgy.*)

My goals in this chapter are to discuss the following concepts:

1) The *properties* of steel that are relevant to knife blades, namely, toughness, hardness, edge retention, wear resistance and corrosion resistance.
2) The basic *processes* that a steel undergoes in an attempt to make it excel in one or more of these properties. This includes the addition of alloys like tungsten, molybdenum or vanadium to the steel and the subsequent *heat treatment* process.
3) What actually happens to the steel during these processes. This will give you some insight as to why the number of possible steels is essentially unlimited and why it is probably impossible to optimize *all* of the aforementioned properties of knife steel at the same time.

In order to accomplish these goals, I will need to briefly discuss the structure of steel and how that structure changes when the steel is heated and cooled in various ways.

As you will see, during the processing of a particular steel, a few degrees of temperature more or less, a few minutes at a given temperature more or less, a few percentage points (by weight) of an alloy such as manganese more or less can make a *significant* difference in the performance of a knife blade.

The Properties of Steel

Even before discussing what steel is, it is important to understand which properties of steel are important in making a good knife blade. Generally speaking, there are several bad things that can happen to a knife blade during use. A blade can

1) crack or chip,
2) wear down, that is *abrade*,
3) bend, that is *deform*,
4) corrode, that is rust or become discolored.

Let us examine these properties in more detail.

 ## *Toughness*

Toughness is the ability of the steel to resist chipping, cracking or fracturing. Put another way, it is the ability of a steel to bend without breaking. It is the opposite of **brittleness**. Common toughness tests include **impact tests**, such as striking the cutting edge (apex) of the blade with a steel rod (cringe!) and **bend fracture tests**, such as measuring the angle through which a knife blade will bend before it snaps.

It is interesting to note that most knife steels are **notch-sensitive**, which means that the presence of a small notch in the steel will make the blade far more sensitive to fracturing near the notch.

I will go into more details about toughness (and ductility) a bit later.

 ## *Hardness*

Hardness is the ability to resist *deformation*. Rather than smashing the edge of a blade with a steel rod to see if the blade will chip, we could *push* the blade's cutting edge into a steel rod to see when and by how much the edge deforms. This is a measure of hardness. (Hardness should not be confused with *hardenability*, a property that I will discuss later.)

Hardness is often measured for knife blades on the **Rockwell C-scale**, abbreviated **HRC**. The steel in folding knives usually falls somewhere in the range of about 58–64 HRC, but most fall in the range 60–62 HRC. Generally speaking, the harder the steel, the less the edge will wear and the better it will retain its edge, but the more brittle it becomes, causing it to be more likely to chip or break. Life is full of tradeoffs! I will discuss other measures of hardness a bit later.

Wear Resistance

Wear resistance is the ability of the steel to withstand *abrasion* due to the friction that the blade encounters when it is used to cut abrasive material such as cardboard, wood or rope. It is also the ability to resist the *adhesion* of foreign particles to the blade. Generally speaking, for a given steel, the harder it is, the more wear resistant it is.

 Edge Retention

A somewhat more imprecise property is **edge retention**, which refers to how long a blade will remain sharp (whatever that means) with use. This property is rather difficult to measure quantitatively, but it would seem to be a consequence of the blade's hardness, toughness and wear resistance all put together.

 Corrosion Resistance

Corrosion resistance is the ability of a steel to withstand corrosion (oxidation) from moisture, humidity and salt.

 Hardness Tests

I think it is useful to discuss some of the different ways in which hardness is measured and to give some specific hardness values for later comparison.

We will see that modern steels contain certain carbon compounds called **carbides**, that is, chemical compounds of carbon and metal. Common examples are tungsten carbide, molybdenum carbide and vanadium carbide. Carbides are much harder than plain steel (iron and carbon) and their presence gives the **alloy steel** used in knife blades its characteristic hardness. Specific hardness values can give us a quantitative idea of the hardness of various carbides. For instance, we will see that vanadium carbide is much harder than either molybdenum carbide or tungsten carbide.

Another reason for looking at specific hardness values is to compare the hardness of sharpening abrasives with the hardness of the steel that they are intended to abrade. For example, two common abrasives are silicon carbide and aluminum oxide. As it happens, silicon carbide is harder than aluminum oxide and so makes a more aggressive sharpening medium. This explains why silicon carbide is used more often in the coarser sharpening stones.

There are many different tests of hardness, with names such as Rockwell A–H, K, N and T, Vickers, Knoop, Mohs, Brinell and Leeb. Each of these tests is appropriate for specific types and shapes of material. For example, some tests are specifically designed for thin materials or for brittle materials or for steels or for ceramics. Although various charts are available to convert one hardness measure to another, since the tests are designed for different purposes, one has to be a bit skeptical about the accuracy of these conversions. In any case, it seems somewhat difficult to compare the hardness of different types of materials unless the materials have been tested by the same method.

Most tests use an **indenter** of a specific shape (for example, a cone, a pyramid or a ball) and composition (for example, diamond or steel) to make an indentation in the material that is being tested. Then some sort of geometric measurement is taken of the resulting indentation to get a numerical value, which is then transformed by a mathematical formula into a hardness measurement.

Hardness measurements must always be taken with a grain of salt. For example, knife blades should really be tested at several different points, not just at one point. Also, hardness tests only reveal the *surface* hardness of a material and not its internal hardness, which may be significantly different.

The Rockwell C-Test for Hardness

As I mentioned earlier, knife blade hardness is generally measured on the **Rockwell C-scale**, abbreviated **HRC**. This test is performed by first applying a **minor load** (penetrating force) to the material to be tested. Then the load is increased by an amount called the **major load**. Finally, the major load is removed, but the minor load is maintained. The "C" in C-test refers to using a 120° diamond cone as the indenter to apply the loads.

The depth of penetration of the major load is measured on a dial. Penetration depth and hardness are inversely proportional and so less penetration (that is, a harder steel) gives a higher number on the Rockwell C-scale.

Actually, each type of knife steel has a recommended hardness *range* within which the steel performs best. For example, for CPM-S30V®, the range is 58-60 and for CPM-M4 the range is 62-64. However, the hardness of the steel of a *particular* knife is determined by the manufacturer during the heat treatment process for that knife (and is presumably within the steel's most effective hardness range). I will describe the heat treatment process a bit later.

The Knoop Test for Hardness

The **Knoop hardness test** is a test used for very brittle or very thin materials, where only small indentations can be permitted. In this test, a pyramidal-shaped diamond is pressed into the material and the indentation is examined under a microscope.

Figure 60 gives some Knoop values. I have also included a few Rockwell C-test values.

Material	Knoop Hardness	HRC
Talc	20	
Silver	60	
Copper	163	
Annealed steel	200	
Pearlite	438	
Glass	530	
Martensite	800	
Quartz	820	
Hardened steel	650–846	56–65
Iron carbide (cementite)	1025	
Chromium carbide	1725	66–68
Molybdenum carbide	1800	72–77
Tungsten carbide	1880	72–77
Aluminum oxide	2100	
Titanium carbide	2470	
Silicon carbide	2480	
Vanadium carbide	2660	82–84
Boron carbide	2750	
Titanium diboride	4400	
Diamond	7000	

Figure 60: Some Knoop/Rockwell hardness values

The Mohs Scale

The **Mohs scale** of hardness is a test that characterizes the **scratch resistance** of one material with respect to another material. Specifically, the Mohs value for a material is determined by what it can scratch and what can scratch it. For example, if a certain material can scratch glass (Mohs 5.5) but is scratched by titanium (Mohs 6), then that material has a Mohs value somewhere between 5.5 and 6. This test is useful in understanding the effectiveness of certain sharpening media (like ceramic or diamond).

Figure 61 shows some typical Mohs values. Unlike the other tests, this test is *qualitative*, not quantitative. That is, the actual Mohs numbers mean *nothing* by themselves but are only meaningful when we compare two Mohs values. For example, a Mohs value of 3 means *only* that material with a higher Mohs values will scratch that material. It would be *incorrect* to say that titanium (Mohs 6), for example, is twice as hard as gold (Mohs 3).

Mohs	Material
1	Talc
2	Calcium
2.5–3	Gold, Silver
3.5	Platinum
4	Nickel, Iron
4–4.5	Steel
5.5	Molybdenum, Glass
6	Titanium, Manganese, Niobium, Rhodium, Silicon, Iron carbide
7	Quartz, Vanadium
8.5	Chromium
9	Aluminum oxide
9.3	Silicon carbide
9–9.5	Tungsten carbide, Vanadium carbide, Titanium carbide
9.5–10	Boron carbide, Boron nitride
10	Diamond

Figure 61: Some Mohs values

 ## A Closer Look at Toughness

Let's take a closer look at the important concept of toughness, for those who are interested.

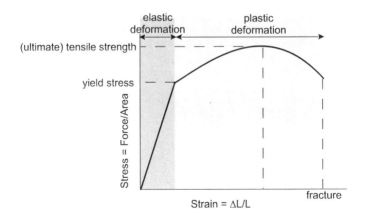

Figure 62: The stress-strain chart

With reference to Figure 62, when a force is applied to a piece of steel, we say that the steel undergoes a *stress*. Technically, **stress** is force per unit cross-sectional area. There are several different types of stress. For example, **tensile stress** is stress applied to an object along an axis that tends to elongate the object, such as pulling on the ends of a steel rod. Other types of stress include compressive stress, bending stress, sheering stress and torsional (rotational) stress.

The reaction of the steel to a stress is called **strain**. Strain is a measure of deformation. For example, when a steel rod is subjected to a tensile stress, it will tend to elongate. In this case, strain is measured as the change ΔL in length of the rod divided by its original length L, that is, $\Delta L/L$. Figure 62 shows the **stress-strain graph** for an application of tensile stress to a metal rod.

If the stress does not exceed a certain value called the **yield stress**, the metal will return to its original size when that stress is removed. During this period, the steel undergoes **elastic deformation**. However, if the stress reaches the yield stress, two things happen.

First, less stress will be required to further elongate the steel and second, the steel will not return to its original length when the stress is removed—it will be permanently elongated. This deformation is called **plastic deformation**. The maximum stress required to continue the deformation of the steel is called the **ultimate tensile strength** or often just the **tensile strength** of the steel.

After the ultimate tensile strength of the steel has been overcome with sufficient stress, less stress will be required to cause the steel to elongate further and eventually fracture, as shown in Figure 62.

Now we can define two important terms. The amount $\Delta L/L$ of elongation that occurs in the steel after the yield strain but before the steel fractures is a measure of the steel's **ductility**. Thus, as shown in Figure 63, a more ductile steel will deform (plastically) more under stress before it breaks, whereas a less ductile (more brittle) steel will break before undergoing much plastic deformation.

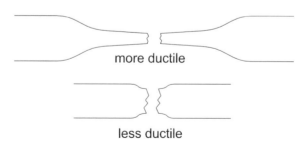

more ductile

less ductile

Figure 63: Ductility

Now, **toughness** is defined to be the area under the entire stress-strain curve. Thus, referring again to Figure 62, toughness has two parts—the width of the stress-strain curve is related to the ductility of the steel and the height is related to the tensile strength. Accordingly, toughness has two components: strength and ductility, that is, the ability of a steel to resist the point of plastic deformation and the ability of a steel to resist fracture after it begins to deform plastically.

 Heat Treating Improves Hardness

To improve hardness, steel undergoes a process called **heat treating**. Here is the heat treating process in brief. I will explain these steps in more detail later.

Preheating

Preheating is the process of heating steel to a certain temperature and holding it at that temperature until all parts of the steel are in thermal equilibrium. Preheating relieves internal stress within the steel and reduces the risk of cracking.

Austenitizing

Austenitizing refers to the process of heating the steel to a very high temperature to change its crystal structure. As we will see, this permits the iron in the steel to absorb more carbon, allowing the final result to be harder and more wear resistant.

Quenching

Quenching refers to the *rapid* cooling of the steel in water or oil to actually harden the steel. However, quenching does make the steel very brittle. In fact, some quenched steel is so brittle that it cracks spontaneously at room temperature!

Tempering

Tempering refers to heating the steel and then cooling it in air in order to toughen the quenched steel. The temperature and length of time used in tempering can significantly effect the final outcome of the steel. Tempering trades some hardness for toughness.

As you can see, several steps are required in heat treating and there is a tradeoff between hardness and toughness. Nevertheless, heat treating basically amounts to repeated heating and cooling of the steel to different degrees and for different periods of time. Note that there are two parameters to each step of this heating/cooling process: *temperature* and *time*. Varying either one of these parameters can have *profound* consequences to the final product, which is why

> *the quality of the heat treatment process has a great deal to do with the final quality of a knife blade.*

 # The Composition of Steel

Iron alone will not make a good knife steel, for it is too soft and too weak. However, adding carbon to steel in very small quantities (say between 0.7% and 3.0% by weight) produces a mixture that is much harder and much tougher than simple iron.

This is accomplished through the heat treating process. However, as always, there is a tradeoff. The higher the concentration of carbon, the more brittle the steel becomes.

 ## *Types of Steel*

Steel can be classified into several groups as follows.

Pure Carbon Steel

I will use the term **pure carbon steel** to refer to a compound composed solely of iron and carbon. It generally does not exist in real-world environments but it will be useful for our discussion to keep things as simple as possible.

Plain Carbon Steel

Practically speaking, along with iron and carbon, most (some say all) modern steels contain small amounts of manganese, along with small amounts of impurities, such as sulfur and phosphorus. These steels are referred to as **plain carbon steels**.

Carbon Steel

Unfortunately, the term **carbon steel** means different things to different people. Some people use the term carbon steel to mean *non-stainless* steel. (I will discuss stainless steel in a moment.) In case you are interested, the *American Iron and Steel Institute (AISI)* defines carbon steel as follows:

> Steel is considered to be carbon steel when no minimum content is specified or required for chromium, cobalt, columbium [niobium], molybdenum, nickel, titanium, tungsten, vanadium or zirconium, or any other element to be added to obtain a desired alloying effect; when the specified minimum for copper does not exceed 0.40 per cent; or when the maximum content specified for any of the following elements does not exceed the percentages noted: manganese 1.65, silicon 0.60, copper 0.60.

How's that for confusing?

Alloy Steel

Elements other than iron and carbon, when added to steel, are called **alloying elements** or simply **alloys**. **Alloy steel** contains one or more additional alloying elements, such as vanadium, tungsten or molybdenum. I will discuss the various alloys that are typically added to knife steel a bit later.

Stainless Steel

Stainless steel is a alloyed steel that contains a specified minimum amount of chromium, which is highly stain resistant. This minimum amount seems to be open to debate. Different sources set this minimum at 10%, 10.5%, 11%, 12%, 13% or even 14% chromium by weight, although as little as 9% chromium will begin to retard corrosion. Note that stainless steel can still stain or corrode under the right (or should I say wrong) conditions, but it does so far less than non-stainless steels.

Rust is iron oxide that forms a film on the steel's surface. However, the formation of iron oxide is *active*, that is, it will continue until the entire piece of steel is turned into rust: It is as though the steel itself was the *food* for an ongoing infectious process. On the other hand, free chromium in the steel forms a *passive* film of chromium oxide that does not spread and so prevents further corrosion, in a manner similar to the formation of a patina in copper.

 The Structure of Pure Iron

To start at the beginning, let me talk first about pure iron.

The atoms of some elements (including carbon and iron) can bond together in different crystal structures known as **allotropes**. For instance, carbon atoms can bond together into an allotrope commonly called **diamond**, which is the most prized allotrope of carbon or an allotrope commonly called **graphite**, which is actually the *most stable* allotrope of carbon. Thus, you may be sad to hear that your diamonds are slowly changing into graphite!

Pure iron in solid form has two distinct allotropes: body-centered and face-centered, as shown in Figure 64.

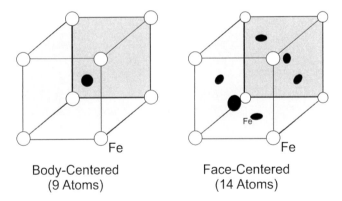

Body-Centered
(9 Atoms)

Face-Centered
(14 Atoms)

Figure 64: The allotropes of iron

The left side of Figure 64 shows the **body-centered structure** of iron crystals, which has 8 iron atoms at the corners of the cube and a ninth iron atom at the center of the cube.

The right side of Figure 64 shows the **face-centered structure** of iron crystals, which has 8 iron atoms at the corners of the cube and an additional 6 iron atoms at the centers of each face of the cube, for a total of 14 atoms of iron. (I made some atoms black and some white just to help envision their location. The white atoms are in the corners of the cube and the black atoms are either in the center or on the faces of the cube. It is hard to draw a good three-dimensional picture in two dimensions.)

Note that the small black and white dots in Figure 64 represent the *centers* of the iron atoms. The atoms themselves are much larger (whatever that means), as shown more accurately for face-centered crystals in Figure 65. The space between atoms is called the **interstitial space**.

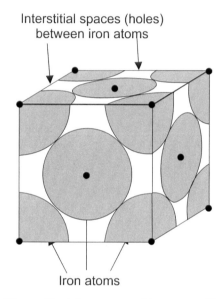

Interstitial spaces (holes)
between iron atoms

Iron atoms

Figure 65: A face-centered iron crystallite

Viewed with less magnification than it takes to see the individual atoms, pure iron that has been heated and cooled forms a *grainy structure*, as shown in Figure 66. Each grain is a microscopic crystal called a **crystallite**, or simply a **grain** by metallurgists. The boundaries between adjacent crystallites are called **grain boundaries**.

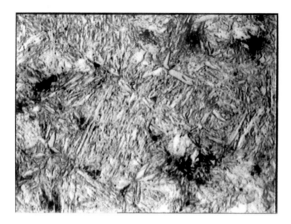

Figure 66: Low carbon (0.35%) water-quenched steel

This brings us to our first remarkable fact about the heating of iron. Below a temperature of 912°C, pure iron has a *body-centered* configuration and is called **ferrite** or **alpha iron** (α-iron). However, above a temperature of 912°C, iron has a *face-centered* configuration and is called **austenite** or **gamma iron** (γ-iron). (Austenite is named after Sir William Chandler Roberts-Austen.) The temperature of 912°C at which grains of iron change from body-centered ferrite to face-centered austenite is called the **transition temperature** of pure iron.

Here is what happens. Heating ferrite to 912°C causes tiny grains of austenite to form within the boundaries between the ferrite grains. As the temperature rises, the austenite grains will grow in number and size and the ferrite grains will decrease in size. Eventually, all that remains is austenite. Moreover, austenite grains are *smaller* than ferrite grains. If we then cool the metal, the reverse process occurs, returning the austenite to ferrite.

You can view an interesting animation of grain growth on Wikipedia at the link

http://en.wikipedia.org/wiki/Grain_growth

In case you are wondering about beta (β) iron (the first three letters of the Greek alphabet being α, β and γ), in the 19th century, scientists theorized the existence of a form of iron with certain properties, which they called beta iron. It was subsequently shown not to exist!

As you might suspect, ferrite and austenite have different properties. For example, ferrite is magnetic but austenite is nonmagnetic. More importantly, austenite can absorb *considerably more* carbon than ferrite and more carbon means more hardness (but also less toughness). The *maximum* solubility of carbon in austenite is 2.14% by weight. For ferrite, it is only 0.022%. (These percentages are temperature-dependent.)

Austenitization is the process of heating pure iron (or steel) to a temperature at which it changes crystal structure from ferrite to austenite.

The Structure of Steel

The terms *ferrite* and *austenite* apply not just to pure iron, but also to pure carbon steel (or plain carbon steel): They simply refer to the configuration of the iron crystals within the steel. The transition temperature of pure carbon steel is lower than that of pure iron: It is 727°C rather than 912°C.

Heating Iron to Make Steel

Pure carbon steel is made by dissolving the smaller carbon atoms into liquid iron. Iron melts at 1540°C and since at that temperature the iron is in its austenitic form, it will readily absorb more carbon. When the resulting liquid solidifies, it generates a **solid solution** containing dissolved carbon atoms within the iron.

The carbon atoms lie in the *interstitial spaces* (*holes*) between the iron atoms of the austenite crystals (above 912°C) or ferrite crystals (below 912°C). Actually, the carbon atoms don't quite fit into the iron crystallites and the iron atoms must part slightly in order to squeeze in the carbon atoms. But there is a limit to how far the iron atoms will separate and this explains why there is a limit to how much carbon can be dissolved in iron. This limit is called the **solubility limit** of the iron.

Nevertheless, as I mentioned earlier, because of their particular crystal structures, austenite, with its bigger interstitial spaces is capable of dissolving far more carbon than ferrite can absorb—in fact about 38.5 times more (at the same temperature)!

When carbon is dissolved in iron, its presence is no longer evident, just as the presence of sugar is no longer evident when dissolved in water. If the amount of dissolved carbon is less than 2.1% by weight, the result is technically called **steel**, but if it is above this value, the result is technically called **cast iron**.

As the table in Figure 75 (coming later) shows, modern knife supersteels tend to have a carbon content ranging from about 1.4% to 3%. I'll bet you didn't know that some of your knife blades are made of cast iron!

What Happens to Excess Carbon: Cementite

The solubility limit of austenite at, say 820°C is 1% (by weight). If an alloy containing 1.5% carbon is heated to 820°C, the excess 0.5% carbon binds with some of the iron atoms to form the chemical compound **iron carbide**, whose chemical formula is Fe_3C (one atom of carbon for every 3 atoms of iron). Iron carbide *in this context* is called **cementite**. Thus, the heated steel mixture contains grains of austenite with dissolved carbon and grains of cementite.

The crystal structure of cementite is more complicated than that of body-centered ferrite or face-centered austenite but fortunately we do not need to go into any details here.

 Two Experiments

Let us consider two experiments. First, we heat 1095 steel (a type of steel) that contains 0.95% carbon to 760°C. As shown in Figure 67, experimental evidence suggests that the cementite forms into small, spherically shaped grains distributed fairly randomly over the austenite grains, which are much larger and have irregular boundaries.

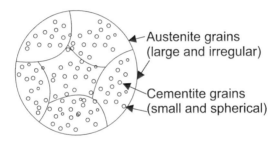

Figure 67: Austenite/cementite structure

As a second experiment, we heat the same 1095 steel to 820°C for 20 minutes and then lower the temperature to 760°C, the temperature in the first experiment. In this case, the resulting grain structure is shown in Figure 68.

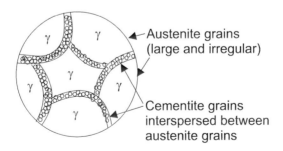

Figure 68: Austenite/cementite structure

In both experiments, the final microstructure has the same *austenite* grain configuration and the same *amount* of both austenite and cementite. However, the *distribution* of the cementite gains is quite different in the two experiments. In the second case, the cementite forms in the grain boundaries of the austenite, rather than randomly throughout the austenite structure.

Now, since cementite is *very brittle*, unlike austenite, you can doubtless see the consequences of using each of the heat treatments on the final outcome of a knife blade. This is a clear example of how heat treatment can change microstructure, which in turn can change the mechanical properties of the final product.

 # Heat Treatment of Steel

Now let us take a closer look at the heat treatment process. The heat treatment process changes the grain structure of the steel—new grains may form and old grains may grow or shrink. Steels can be classified as **fine grained**, **medium grained** or **coarse grained**. The grain structure of a steel has a profound effect on the steel's performance, as well as its sharpenability. In general, finer grained steels can take a sharper edge and a narrower cutting bevel angle than coarser grained steel. Have you every tried to put a fine edge on a piece of concrete?

Knife steel is usually supplied in an annealed condition with a hardness of only about HRC 20 to facilitate workability. The heat treating process proceeds as follows.

 ## *Preheating*

Preheating is the process of heating steel to a certain temperature and holding it at that temperature until all parts of the steel are in thermal equilibrium. Preheating relieves internal stress within the steel and reduces the risk of cracking. It also reduces the inevitable changes in size that steel undergoes during the heat treatment process. (Steel changes in size by about 0.0005–0.002 inch per inch of original length during heat treatment.)

Preheating also reduces the time that the steel must remain at the higher austenitizing temperature. Extended time at the higher temperature increases grain size and can lead to additional brittleness in the steel.

 ## *Austenitizing*

Austenitizing refers to the process of heating the steel to a temperature at which it changes its crystal structure from ferrite to austenite. Austenitizing is important because austenite can absorb considerably more carbon than can ferrite and carbon is essential for increased edge retention, tensile strength, hardness and resistance to wear and abrasion. In general, higher austenitizing temperatures produce somewhat higher hardness and lower temperatures produce somewhat higher toughness.

However, it is important to keep the grain size of steels as small as possible in order to improve the toughness of the steel. But grain growth is very sensitive to temperature, being faster at higher temperatures and this is why it is important not to austenitize at temperatures any higher than necessary.

 Quenching

What happens when austenitized steel is allowed to cool? This depends on how *rapidly* it cools. Let us first consider what happens if the steel is cooled slowly.

Slow Cooling of Steel

When face-centered austenite cools, it transforms into body-centered ferrite. If the cooling process is sufficiently slow, the carbon atoms that lay within the interstitial spaces of the austenite grains have time to escape before the iron trap closes. These carbon atoms will combine with iron to form cementite (Fe_3C).

This cementite will form a grain structure that is composed of alternating layers of cementite (Fe_3C) and pure iron (Fe), called **pearlite**. Pearlite is relatively soft, with a Knoop hardness value of about 438. Figure 69 shows a grain of pearlite.

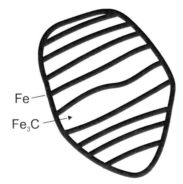

Figure 69: Pearlite

Figure 70 shows a micrograph of pearlite taken with a scanning electron microscope. The alternating light-dark layered portions in the figure are grains of pearlite. The darker portion in the figure is additional crystalline cementite (iron carbide) that forms between the grains of pearlite. (If the original carbon content was below 0.8%, the iron carbide between the pearlite is ferrite, not cementite. However, this is not relevant to most knife blades.)

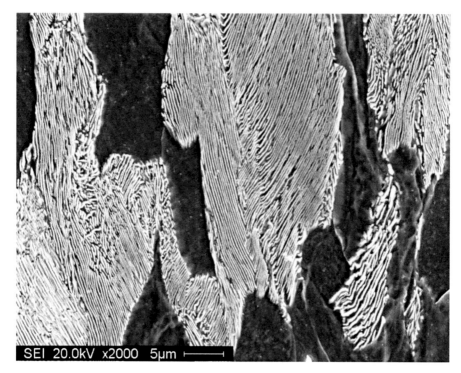

Figure 70: Micrograph showing (etched) pearlite (2000x)

Rapid Cooling of Steel: Quenching

Rapid cooling of a metal is called **quenching**. Quenching is usually done by immersing the metal in water or oil. One of the most fascinating properties of steel is that it can be strengthened to amazingly high levels by quenching. Indeed, the strength of quenched steel can reach over twice that of titanium!

If austenite is cooled very rapidly, as in quenching, there is not enough time for the carbon atoms to escape the interstitial spaces of the austenite grains to form pearlite. Instead, a new very hard structure is formed, called **martensite** (named after the German metallurgist Adolf Martens). In contrast to pearlite, with a Knoop value of around 438, martensite has a Knoop value of about 800 and so is much harder than pearlite.

Because there was not time for an orderly transition from austenite to ferrite, the crystal structure of the resulting martensite is different than that of ferrite. More specifically, the martensite crystallites are elongated rectangular solids (with square bases), as shown in Figure 71.

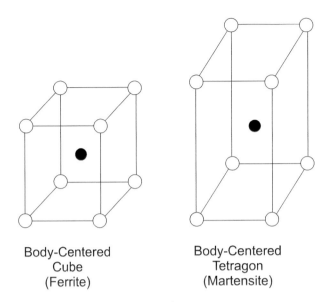

Body-Centered   Body-Centered
Cube   Tetragon
(Ferrite)   (Martensite)

Figure 71: Ferrite and martensite structure

In fact, the higher the concentration of carbon, the taller the tetragon becomes.

Thus, we can say that the *rate* at which a steel is cooled makes a considerable difference in the final structure of the steel and therefore effects the mechanical properties of the steel. Moreover, the end result of heat treating the high-carbon steel used in knife making is martensite.

Hardenability

Quenching does not guarantee that the *entire piece* of steel will become fully martenistic. **Hardenability** is a measure of how deep below the surface a quenched steel can be made martensitic. (This should not be confused with *hardness*, which is a measure of susceptibility to penetration.)

 Tempering

While quenching does harden the steel considerably, it also leaves the steel *very brittle* and puts it under great stress. If used in this condition, a just-quenched steel would likely shatter. In fact, some steels will crack spontaneously in this condition at room temperature. Therefore, once the steel has been quenched to about 52°C, it should be *tempered* immediately.

Tempering is done by heating the steel to a certain temperature range for a certain period of time (often 2–4 hours), then allowing it to cool in still air. Tempering reduces hardness somewhat but greatly increases the toughness of the steel. The final properties of the steel can be controlled by adjusting the temperature and time of the tempering.

While the end result of rapid cooling (quenching) is martensite, some austenite (sometimes as much as half) is still retained in the quenched steel. Repeated tempering may be necessary in order to convert this retained austenite into untempered martensite and then finally into tempered martensite.

The Effect of Carbon on Toughness and Hardness

Effect on Toughness

Figure 72 shows the effect of carbon content on toughness. Steel with lots of carbon (roughly 0.9% and higher) is stronger in the sense that the yield stress is higher and so the steel can recover its shape after being subjected to higher stresses. Steels with very little carbon (roughly 0.3% and less) are the most ductile, that is, they can withstand more plastic deformation before fracturing, but their yield strength is not as great. Steels with moderate carbon content (roughly 0.3% to 0.9%) are toughest, that is, they combine both strength and ductility better than high or low carbon steels.

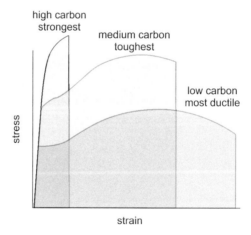

Figure 72: Effect of carbon content on toughness

We can now understand why fixed blade knives generally have a lower carbon content than folders. Fixed blade knives are intended to be used in a combat, survival or wilderness setting where the last thing you want is for the blade to snap when stabbing or prying. Thus, toughness is a priority for fixed blade knives. On the other hand, folders are more apt to be used for slicing and general cutting, rather than stabbing and prying. Hence, they are not subject to as high stresses as fixed blade knives.

For example, CPM 3V steel is extremely tough and has a carbon content of 0.8%. The steel denoted by 1095 is frequently used in fixed blade knives and has a carbon content of 0.90%–1.03%. On the other hand, ZDP-189, a common high-end supersteel used in folders, has a carbon content of 3.00%. Figure 75 (coming later) shows that the carbon content of many modern supersteels falls in the range from 1.42% to 3.00%.

As I will discuss later, one of the reasons to add alloying elements, such as molybdenum and vanadium to high-carbon steel is to increase its toughness.

 ## *Effect on Hardness*

Considering the superior toughness of low and medium carbon steels, you may wonder what are the advantages to high carbon steels. *Probably the main reason for the use of high carbon steels is because of their improved wear resistance.*

Indeed, the hardness (and strength) of steel increases dramatically with higher concentrations of carbon. One way to think of the reason for this is to think of the chemical bonds holding the iron atoms together as springs. As the precentage of carbon increases, the springs are stretched more and more by the intervening carbon atoms, thereby making it more difficult to extend them farther, that is, making the structure harder.

Figure 73 shows a graph of the hardness of fresh martensite, as measured by the Rockwell C scale, as a function of carbon content. The hardness reaches its peak at about HRC 66 when the carbon content is about 0.8% by weight.

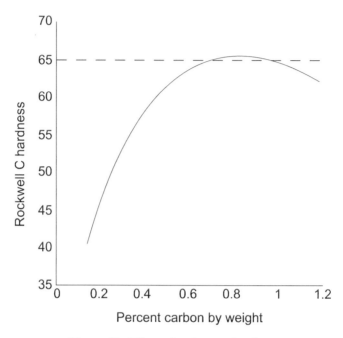

Figure 73: Effect of carbon on hardness

The dip in hardness when the concentration of carbon exceeds 0.8% is due to the presence of retained austenite.

In summary, increasing the carbon content of steel results in decreased toughness but increased strength (able to withstand more stress before being deformed plastically), increased hardness and increased wear resistance.

However, the quenching process severely lowers toughness and this effect must be countered through the tempering process, which can severly effect hardness. The stage is now set to discuss alloy steel.

 # Alloy Steel

Thus far, our discussion has concentrated on pure carbon steel in order to keep things as simple as possible. Let us now consider the effect of adding additional alloys to steel.

 ## *The Effects of Alloys on the Properties of Steel*

Simply put, the addition of alloys changes the crystal structure of the resulting steel and so causes profound changes in the steel's mechanical properties. Of course, the general purpose of alloying steel is to *improve* its mechanical properties.

Two of the most important specific reasons for adding alloys to steel are to improve hardenability and to improve the results of tempering by *reducing the loss of hardness*.

The amount of alloy added to pure carbon steel ranges from 1% to 50% by weight. Just which alloys to add and at what quantities is "big business" in the steel game. According to Figure 75 (coming later), the most common alloys in the major super steels are manganese, chromium, molybdenum, and vanadium.

Here is a rundown of the effects of several alloys. The alloys listed have different levels of effectiveness, of course. Also, it is often true that small amounts of a particular alloy have a desirable effect but larger amounts have a detrimental effect. This list is meant only as a *rough guide*.

Increases Hardness

Carbon, molybdenum, tungsten, vanadium, phosphorus, cobalt, nickel

Increases Toughness

Molybdenum, nickel, niobium, tungsten, vanadium, phosphorus, cobalt, silicon, chromium

Increases Wear Resistance

Carbon, manganese, molybdenum, chromium

Increases Corrosion Resistance

Chromium, copper (in small amounts), niobium

Increases Hardenability

Chromium, manganese, tungsten, boron, molybdenum

Reduces Grain Size

Molybdenum, niobium, vanadium

Reduces Brittleness

Manganese

Increases Brittleness

Carbon, phosphorus

Increases Workability

Sulfur (but decreases toughness)

As you can see from the previous list, alloys have several effects on the outcome of the heat treatment process.

 *Hardness*

Recall that when pure carbon steel is heated to high temperatures, any excess carbon will bond to iron to produce iron carbide, also called cementite.

However, when alloys such as vanadium, molybdenum and tungsten are added to pure carbon steel, carbon atoms will bond to these alloys rather than to iron because these carbides *are more stable* than iron carbide. Thus, the heat treatment process will produce carbides such as vanadium carbide, molybdenum carbide and tungsten carbide rather than iron carbide.

Now, a glance at Figure 74 shows that the carbides and especially vanadium carbide are far harder and far more scratch resistant than iron carbide. No wonder the presence of one or more of these alloys will improve the quality of a knife blade.

Material	Knoop	Mohs
iron carbide (cementite)	1025	6
molybdenum carbide	1800	9
tungsten carbide	1880	9
vanadium carbide	2660	9

Figure 74: A telling tale

 *Hardenability*

We have seen that when plain steel is quenched, austenite is converted to martensite because the carbon atoms do not have time to make an orderly exit form the iron lattice. This is an **allotropic transformation**, that is, a change in the crystal structure of the material.

The presence of alloys, such as vanadium, molybdenum and tungsten, have a profound effect on the results of heat treatment because they tend to slow down the diffusion of atoms through the iron lattices and thereby delay or alter allotropic transformations. In plain terms, *alloying elements affect the crystal structure of the steel and therefore also its physical properties.*

One implication of this is that martensite, which is normally produced by rapid quenching, can be produced at slower rates of cooling, which puts much less stress on the material and more importantly, *improves hardenability.*

 Tempering

As we have seen, tempering is required to reduce toughness, that is, to make the steel less brittle. However, tempering causes the hardness to drop. As mentioned earlier, one of the most important reasons for adding alloys to steel is to reduce the loss of hardness incurred by tempering.

Powder Metallurgy (PM)

The traditional steel making process begins by **annealing** the steel, specifically by melting the steel and then allowing it to cool *slowly*. This process makes the steel more workable. (Knife makers can buy steel that has already been annealed.)

While in its molten state, the steel is highly homogeneous but because it is allowed to cool slowly, the alloys in the steel have a tendency to *segregate*, resulting in a non-uniform microstructure. Additional processing is therefore required to refine the microstructure, but the segregation effects are never completely eliminated.

Powder metallurgy (or **PM**) is a process for producing steel that mitigates the segregation problem. The PM process begins by *atomizing* the homogenous molten steel into fine droplets. Specifically, the molten metal is poured through a small nozzle where high pressure gas disburses the liquid into a spray of tiny spherical droplets. These droplets solidify *rapidly* into powder particles—so rapidly that *segregation is suppressed*.

The powder is then pressed into the desired shape, a process called **compacting**. The compacted steel is then heated in order to bond the material, a process called **sintering**. In some PM processes, such as that of Crucible Industries, the compacting and sintering processes are combined into a single process called **hot isostatic pressing (HIP)**.

The resulting sintered steel may undergo additional processing, including repressing, resintering and heat treating.

Steel Brands

With the possible addition of several different alloys in different concentrations and the possible variation in the heat-treating process, it should come as no surprise that the number of possible steel compositions is essentially limitless.

On a practical level, opinions vary quite a bit as to which steel composition performs best for various applications. One complicating issue is that the performance of any particular type of steel will depend in large part on the *quality* of the manufacturing process.

Nevertheless, in shopping for a knife, you must begin somewhere. So here is a partial and certainly debatable grouping of some brands of steel used in knives that will at least give you that starting point.

CPM® refers to *Crucible Industries* powder metal process known as **Crucible Particle Metallurgy** and **CTS**® refers to the **Carpenter Technology**® family of steel alloys. ZDP-189 is a Japanese steel from Hitachi. Elmax® and M390 are manufactured by Böhler Uddeholm. The term "quality" refers to an elusive combination of properties such as toughness, edge retention, wear resistance, hardness and corrosion resistance. (Is that vague enough?) Note that the only steel in this list that is *not* stainless is M4, because it contains only 4% chromium.

Highest Quality "Supersteels"

CPM S90V
M390
ZDP-189
Elmax
CTS-XHP
CTS-204P

Very High Quality

CPM M4 (not stainless)
CPM S35VN
CPM S30V

High Quality

154CM
CPM154 (CPM-manufactured version of Crucible's 154 CM)
ATS-34
D2
VG-10
H1
N680

Almost High Quality

440C
AUS-8
8Cr13MoV
14C28N

Figure 75 is a table of alloy compositions for the top steels. This table is also meant as a *rough guide* to give you a sense of the relative amounts of alloys in some knife steels. Note that some of the steels are *very* similar, for instance, M390 and CTS-204P.

	C	Cr	V	Mo	W	Mn	Si	S	Nb	Ni
CPM S90V	2.30	14.00	9.00	1.00						
M390	1.90	20.00	4.00	1.00	0.60	0.30	0.70			
CTS-204P	1.90	20.00	4.00	1.00	0.65	0.35	0.60			
ZDP-189	3.00	20.00	0.10	1.40	0.60	0.50	0.40			
Elmax	1.70	18.00	3.00	1.00		0.30	0.40			
CTS-XHP	1.60	16.00	0.45	0.80		0.50	0.40			0.35
CPM M4	1.42	4.00	4.00	5.25	5.50	0.30		0.06		
CPM S35VN	1.45	14.00	3.00	2.00					0.50	
CPM S30V	1.45	14.00	4.00	2.00						

Figure 75: Table of steel compositions (numbers are percentages)

Figure 76 shows a chart from Crucible Industries' web site indicating the relative properties of some of their steels.

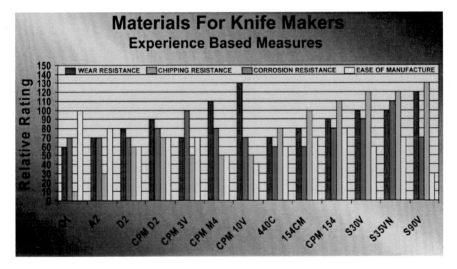

Figure 76: A steel properties chart (Courtesy of Crucible Industries)

As you can see, if wear resistance is your most important consideration, then the top steels are (in order)

CMP V10
S90V
CPM M4
S35VN and S30V

For toughness (resistance to chipping) the top steels are (in order)

S35VN
CPM 3V
S30V
CPM 154, CPM M4 and CPM D2

Therefore, according to this chart, no one steel is best for all purposes! I guess we already knew that by now.

 ## So Is This Steel Good?

Suppose you find a knife that you really like and the steel is Brand X. How do you decide if this steel will suit your needs? That's a tough question.

As an example, I recently talked with a custom knife maker who uses 80CrV2 steel for a knife that interested me, so let's use that steel as an example. He told me that he chose that steel based on his experience as a knifemaker, which I assume is considerable. The knife in question is a fixed blade knife, but the principal is the same for folders. I should point out that for a fixed blade knife, my main concern is toughness—I don't want my knife blade to snap while I am prying with the blade or deform when I am batoning.

I immediately did a search for 80CrV2 using The Google. There I encountered two types of web sites, which I will call *data sites* and *opinion sites*. The first hit I got was a data site, namely, a supplier of 80CrV2 steel called Bestar. On that site, I found a chemical analysis of the steel (the numbers are percentages)

C: 0.75–0.85
Si: 0.15–0.35
Mn:0.30–0.50
P: 0.025
Cr: 0.40-0.60
V: 0.15–0.25

as well as some data on heat treating, neither of which was terribly helpful to my purchasing decision. Of course, the low chromium content told me that this is certainly not stainless steel. I was glad to see that there is some vanadium in the steel, but it isn't anywhere near as much as the supersteels in Figure 75, so I wasn't sure how significant this quantity of vanadium is to the steel's performance as a knife blade.

The web site also briefly discusses uses for this steel:

> Low alloy tool steel for cold work. Primarily used for carbide tipped saw bodies, circular saw blades, solid tooth saw bodies for agricultural use, pruning blades, gardening tools, friction saws, frame saws and log saws (paper roll cutting).

I must admit that this was a bit discouraging. I certainly don't want to spend a lot of money on a custom knife whose steel is primarily suited to gardening tools! Yet, why would a highly regarded custom knife maker use such a steel if it did not excel in some way as a knife blade? Clearly, at this point I needed more information.

The next hit a got from my Google search was BladeForums.com, a very popular forum devoted to knives. It appears that someone was given a hunk of this steel and wanted information about heat treating. Again, not useful to me. There were a few comments comapring this steel to other steels I had never heard of. Also not useful.

The web site zknives.com is also very popular and has a lot of information about knives, so that was my next stop. However, aside from the chemical composition of the steel, which incidentally differs somewhat from that given by the supplier I mentioned above, I could not find any helpful information about the steel's performance as a knife blade.

Finally, I turned to YouTube, where I found these stress-test videos:

> https://www.youtube.com/watch?v=mp7XM7g8tdg
> https://www.youtube.com/watch?v=jiuUHUAaj_c
> https://www.youtube.com/watch?v=m5B250kMuCA

I concluded that this is one tough steel, which is what I was looking for in a fixed-blade knife. Of course, I have the usual reservation that the quality of a particular knife blade depends to a very large extent on the quality of the heat treating process that it underwent. However, putting some faith in the reputation of the knifemaker, I bought the knife.

I think that the moral of this little tale is that if you have doubts about a steel, you will need to do some research and you will also need to get lucky that you find useful and reliable information.

Finally, I must suggest being *very careful* about believing what you read on the Internet. You may find this surprising, but not everyone who voices an opinion knows what they are talking about!

Knife Sharpening

My guess is that most knife users wish that they would never need to sharpen a knife. On the other hand, I would also guess that many knife enthusiasts like to sharpen, for they are on a quest for that elusive "ultimate edge." Personally, I like to sharpen. Like many, I find it to be a relaxing endeavor (at least most of the time). Of course, for me, it is a hobby. If I depended on sharp knives to make a living, I might feel a bit different. I also wonder how many knife users who say they don't like to sharpen would change their mind if they were more successful at sharpening. Perhaps this chapter will help.

Actually, sharpening is a relatively complex issue. There are a many different types of sharpening systems on the market and far more opinions on which system is best. My plan is to acquaint you with the general issues involved in sharpening *as I see them*, along with many of the more prominent sharpening systems, including using no system at all (called *freehand sharpening*).

Of course, one alternative to sharpening your own knives is to simply send them back to the manufacturer or to a local knife shop for sharpening. Many knife manufacturers offer free lifetime sharpening. (Of course, whether or not that service is *really* free is open to debate.)

If that is your preference, then your sharpening problems are solved, although this approach does have its own set of problems. First, you will need to carefully package and ship your knife or at least transport it to a local knife store. Second, you will be without the knife for at least a day and possibly a week or so. Third, if the service is not free, you will need to pay for it *every time* your knife needs sharpening. Fourth, it is very unlikely that for the few dollars you are willing to pay to have a knife sharpened (or for the free service), the sharpener is going to spend one to two hours fine tuning your blade! Put another way, you can get *far better results* if you do it yourself. Frankly, if I could not sharpen my own knives, I would think twice about even using my knives.

 ## So You're Happy With The Factory Edge?

It has been my experience that knives that come with a factory edge are, shall we say, less than ideally sharp. Actually, I have noticed quite a variation in the sharpness of knives right out of the box and I have been surprised that some $40 knives are far sharper out of the box than some $200 knives. Nevertheless, I have never seen a factory edge that approached the sharpness that one can get with a proper sharpening. Somewhat surprisingly, this is also true of the expensive custom knives that I have encountered. In fact, I have *never* met a new knife that I felt did not need some sharpening and the vast majority of them needed a complete reprofiling and resharpening.

To illustrate, Figure 77 shows a micrograph that I took of a brand new $200 knife. The even, perfectly perpendicular (to the cutting edge) scratch pattern on the bevel is characteristic of a belt sharpener (which is not in itself a bad thing) and you can see a few small imperfections in the apex. Still, the knife did cut modestly well.

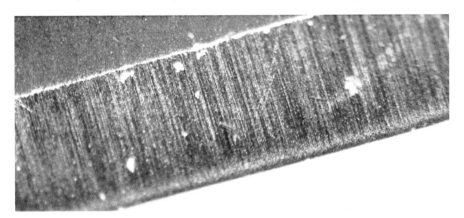

Figure 77: A factory edge

On the other hand, Figure 78 shows the bevel after I sharpened the knife. In this case, I used a KME sharpener, starting with a coarse diamond stone and working through to a strop endowed with a very fine polishing compound. I probably don't need to tell you that the cutting performance improved immensely. (The few larger scratches that remain in the bevel are typical of a custom sharpening and have no real effect on cutting performance.)

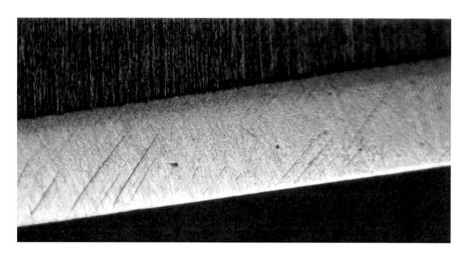

Figure 78: The bevel after custom sharpening

Types of Sharpening Methods

I like to group sharpening methods into three categories.

Freehand Sharpening

By **freehand sharpening**, I mean holding the knife in your hand and rubbing the cutting bevel back and forth against a stationary abrasive medium, such as a ceramic or diamond stone. Alternatively, the knife can be fixed in a clamp and the stone can be rubbed over the blade. This approach is not nearly as common, but I have found it to be very helpful in certain situations. I often use it, for example, to sharpen my hatchets.

Let me be very clear at the outset—*freehand sharpening takes a lot of practice and can be quite frustrating at the beginning.* However, I will have a suggestion for you that may ease the learning curve.

In order to do freehand sharpening, you will need an abrasive **stone set** consisting of somewhere between two (better: three) and six stones of varying levels of abrasiveness. As I will discuss later, there are various options here. For example, Figure 79 shows a set of Shapton glass ceramic stones, viewed from the back side of the stones. (The front is pure white.) Figure 80 shows a coarse DMT diamond stone.

Figure 79: A Shapton Glass Stone® set (back view)

Figure 80: A coarse DMT diamond stone

The trick in freehand sharpening is to maintain a *consistent* **sharpening angle**, that is, the angle between the cutting bevel and the sharpening stone, a subject I will discuss in some detail later. You should also take care to maintain a consistent bevel thickness along the entire cutting edge and to sharpen both sides of the cutting edge as equally as possible.

 Assisted Sharpening Systems

By an **assisted sharpening system**, I mean a sharpening system that uses a jig or guide of some kind that helps (or forces) you to maintain a consistent sharpening angle. I will discuss three such systems: the Edge Pro, the Wicked Edge and the KME.

 Motorized Sharpening Systems

By a **motorized sharpening system**, I mean a sharpening system that uses a motor to move the sharpening medium, whether or not it has a guide for helping to maintain a consistent angle. Examples are the Tormek (a large but *very slow* moving abrasive wheel) and the Work Sharp (a small, variable speed belt sander). I will discuss the

Work Sharp but not the Tormek because I do not believe that it is the best choice for sharpening small folding knives.

Incidentally, I would *never* take a knife to a high-speed grinder, although I know some people who do. I use a high-speed grinder to sharpen my lathe turning tools and I know from experience that a grinder can chew up or overheat a knife *very quickly*. High speed grinders rotate dry at around 3000 rpm; the Tormek rotates at 90 rpm through a water bath!

 # Sharpening Is Very Personal

Possibly the only thing I can say with absolute certainty about sharpening is that it is a *highly personal* process. For every reasonable approach to sharpening, there are probably many people who would say that this is the best approach. I think that there is currently no one best approach. Each has its advantages and disadvantages, like most things in life.

Over the past 30 years, I have used a variety of abrasives, including

- Oil stones
- Japanese waterstones
- Shapton Glass Stones
- Naniwa Chosera stones
- Edge Pro ceramic stones
- Spyderco ceramic stones
- DMT and Atoma Diamond stones

I have also used a variety of assisted and motorized sharpening systems, including the Edge Pro, the KME, the Work Sharp, the Wicked Edge and the Tormek.

While I regard my role in this book as primarily providing *information* so that you can make your own decisions, I will still offer you my opinions here and there, for whatever they are worth. If your opinions differ from mine on matters for which you have some experience (a distinct possibility), *please do not be offended*. I acknowledge that my opinion is only that—*an opinion*.

 # Sharpening Frustration

Sharpening, even with an assisted or motorized system but especially freehand is definitely a *skill* and as such, it takes time to learn.

In general, your goal is to produce an even, mirror-polished bevel, like the ones shown in Figure 81 and Figure 82. The micrograph insertion in Figure 81 shows that it is difficult to remove *all* of the scratches in the bevel. I spent about 30–40 minutes sharpening this knife. I could have removed more scratches by spending more time sharpening, but there is clearly a diminishing return here. This bevel is past razor sharp and I can see the individual hairs of my beard in its reflection. That is generally enough for me.

Figure 81: A sharpened bevel with an even, mirror polish

Figure 82: A mirror polish

I often think back some 30 years ago when I tried to sharpen my first plane blade using oil stones and a small jig for holding the blade. The result was supposed to be a blade that would take beautiful, fine shavings on the order of a thousandth of an inch from a piece of wood, as shown in Figure 83. Instead, all I got was some ugly wood dust—and not even much of that!

Figure 83: A sharp plane blade produces beautiful shavings

It took me some time to finally get a passable edge on a plane blade and a lot more time to get a professional edge. It will probably take you some time as well. If you get any satisfaction from the process of sharpening, stick with it. Try not to get too discouraged. Who knows, soon you may be hiring yourself out for a few extra bucks as a knife sharpener! At the very least, you will become more popular with your friends and neighbors.

One thing I would strongly urge is that before spending any money on a particular sharpening system, you watch as many YouTube sharpening videos as you can stand. All you need to do is search for the name of the system or stone, for example, you can search for "freehand sharpening", "Wicked Edge" or "Chosera stones". You should also watch any videos from the companies that make the systems. (These are usually posted on YouTube as well.) This is the best way to see these systems in action, something I cannot provide to you in this book. In this way, at least you may be able to eliminate some systems from your short list.

Practical Versus Theoretical Sharpening

I think it is important to divide sharpening into two camps, which I will call **practical sharpening** and **theoretical sharpening**.

In practical sharpening, all we want to do is get an edge that is *sharp enough* (or perhaps a little more☺) to do what we need it to do for as long as possible. We do not care if the knife could be a lot sharper, because we realize that the sharper the knife is, the shorter it will remain that sharp. Also, we do not care if the bevel is so highly polished that we can distinguish every individual hair on our faces in the reflection. In this context, sharpening is a practical necessity, not a luxury. Also, for this purpose, our bevel angles tend to be a little larger.

In theoretical sharpening, we are in quest of that **ultimate edge**, regardless of the consequences. We do not care if a single swipe through a piece of cardboard will remove that edge. Moreover, we definitely want to see each of those hairs reflected in the bevel!

I suspect that 95% or more of knife users are not interested in theoretical sharpening!

I also suspect that those of us who are interested in getting that ultimate edge want to do so only on a few of our "higher-end" knives, because we realize that such an edge is fleeting and therefore not really all that useful (unless of course you routinely shave with your folders).

Even though many of the knives we buy are intended for real use cutting up cardboard boxes, Manila rope, twist ties and so on, being knife aficionados and not just mere knife users, we can't quite settle for "just sharp enough." Instead, we want something that falls somewhere between a practical edge and an ultimate edge—at least sharp enough to impress both ourselves and our friends. We appreciate the title "expert sharpener."

In the upcoming discussion, I am going to address myself to both practical and theoretical sharpening. For the most part, practical sharpening and theoretical sharpening use the same equipment and the same methods. The main exception is that a practical sharpener will not use the ultra-fine abrasives designed to approximate that ultimate edge. But the sharpening *techniques* are the same.

It is also important to keep in mind that you can approach even practical sharpening at various levels of involvement. If you feel that you have better things to do than sharpen blades, you can simply invest in a single sharpening system and a strop and get to know it well. With practice—how much no one can say—you will no doubt become an accomplished sharpener using that system.

I think that the vast majority of practical knife users will be perfectly happy with this approach and need go no further into the intricacies of sharpening. However, if you enjoy the sharpening process, you will want to delve more deeply into this art form.

You may even want to eventually invest in more than one stone set and/or sharpening system.

At the most theoretical level, you can pour over microscopic pictures of knife edges, looking at scratch patterns and ruminating over such intricate questions as the following:

- How do microfractures occur and how can I avoid them?
- Is a toothy edge better than a smooth edge?
- Can I get a level 5 hanging hair test result form my ultimate edge?
- Instead of following (say) a Shapton 1000 grit stone with the Shapton 8000 grit stone as some "experts" recommend, should I follow it by the 2000 grit stone, then the 4000 grit and then the 6000 grit stone? Or maybe skip the 4000? Or maybe skip the 2000 and 6000 instead and use the 4000? Erg!
- Perhaps it would be better after using the Shapton 8000 to switch to a Chosera 10000 rather than the Shapton 16000? Is the Chosera 10000 "better" than the Shapton 16000?
- Is green stropping compound better than white compound or yellow compound or pink compound?
- Should I strop below 0.5 micron grit size? Does a 25 nanometer emulsion improve the edge over a 50 nanometer emulsion? What about stropping with no compound?
- Should I use cow hide, horse butt, kangaroo, balsa wood or nano cloth to strop?
- Should I consolidate the edge when I am done with the entire sharpening process?

As long as you get some *joy* out of searching for that perfect edge, there is no harm in pursuing these questions (other than to your pocket book, of course). But you should keep in mind that chasing the ultimate edge is more of a hobby (unless you are in the sharpening business) than a practical necessity.

 # What is Sharpness?

Let me discuss three concepts that I think are sometimes confused with each other by people new (and not new) to the sharpening process, namely, *sharpening*, *bevel polishing* and *cutting performance*.

 ## *Sharpness*

Besides being an English port in Gloucestershire, we can say that **sharpness** is a measure of how closely the two surfaces of the cutting bevel meet at their apex. For example, between the two cutting edges in Figure 84, the one on the left would seem to be sharper.

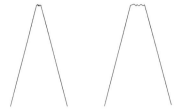

Figure 84: The edge on the left appears sharper

Of course, the two planes of the cutting bevel can never meet in a true straight line because steel is *grainy*.

Cutting Bevel Polish

Polishing the cutting bevel of a blade is obviously not the same as narrowing the apex of the blade. However, the sharpening process inevitably involves doing both of these things *at the same time*—you cannot narrow the apex of a blade without affecting the adjacent cutting bevel nor polish the bevel without narrowing the apex of the blade *to some extent*.

Cutting Performance

It is important not to loose sight of the fact that sharpness and bevel polish are not all there is to **cutting performance**. In fact, the state of polish of the bevel probably has only a minor effect on cutting performance—even though friction is reduced, the cutting bevel is generally very narrow and so this reduction is not very significant.

Other factors that effect cutting performance are bevel angle and the *smoothness* of the apex. As shown in Figure 85, a perfectly narrow apex (if there was such a thing) can be relatively smooth or it can be **toothy**.

Smooth edge   Toothy edge

Figure 85: Smooth and toothy edges

There is some debate over which type of edge is best in various circumstances. The conventional wisdom seems to be that a toothy edge is better for kitchen slicing knives, for example, because the apex of the blade acts like a tiny saw, sawing through recalcitrant foods like tomato and onion skins. But if that is the case, then a toothy edge is probably better in some other situations as well. Just food for thought.

Another aspect of cutting performance is the thickness of the knife blade itself. You can put a razor-sharp, hair-shaving edge on a large tactical knife with a 1/4-inch thick blade, but it will not slice a fat carrot very well because even though the cutting edge will easily penetrate the surface of the carrot, the thick blade will act like a wedge and try to force apart the two sections of the carrot. As a result, the resistance that the knife receives from the carrot will make it difficult for the cutting edge to advance farther into the kerf.

How you sharpen your knives (bevel angle, apex smoothness, etc.) depends to a large extent on how you use them. However, setting all of this aside, the topic of this chapter is how to get the smoothest, narrowest apex and most highly polished bevel possible on a knife, whatever the bevel angle or thickness of the blade. If you don't want a particular knife to be as sharp or smooth as possible, you will still use the same sharpening materials (for the most part) and the same sharpening procedure I will describe a bit later, but you will just not finish all of the steps!

 # When Is It Sharp?

As with many things related to sharpening, different folks have different answers to this question. I will give you some possible tests of sharpness in a minute. But first a quick story.

Sometime after my sharpening infancy, that is, when I was finally able to get what I thought might be a decent blade, my greatest frustration was not knowing just how sharp my blades were compared to those of an "expert" sharpener. I wondered if I was getting anywhere close to expert results, or if an expert would just laugh at my edges. Put another way, I wondered what "really sharp" really was!

You might think that you could go to a knife store and pay to have someone sharpen one of your knives and then compare it to your own results, but I am very skeptical that you would get a truly expert-level result this way. You might find an expert-level service on line—I haven't really looked for obvious reasons. However, my little story took place *before* the invention of the Internet (but somewhat *after* the invention of the steam engine)!

So I was never able to determine if I was able to get expert sharpening results. In fact, I still don't really know!

Still, here are some tests for sharpness, for whatever they are worth.

 ## *The Phone Book Paper Test*

If you browse YouTube, you will see a lot of sharpening videos that demonstrate sharpness by cutting loose sheets of phone book paper. Pinch a sheet of paper between your thumb and forefinger at the long edge and about one-third of the way from the short edge. Then swipe the knife *away* from you into the paper at an acute angle. Try varying the angle of your cut into the paper. There are two versions of this process. You can use a slicing action as though you were slicing a tomato or a straight pushing action. The **push cut** requires a sharper blade than the **slice cut**.

With this test, you are checking to see if the knife catches in the paper and also the smoothness of the resulting cut. Any catching or rough edges indicate a nonsharp knife or a defect in the apex of the blade. You can also detect a certain level of resistance: The sharper the blade, the less resistance until you get to the point where it seems almost as though the paper wasn't even there! (This is not easy to achieve.) You can also *hear* the difference between a sharp blade and a *really* sharp blade—the quieter the cutting sound, the sharper the blade.

Phone book paper has a grain direction (usually but not always running lengthwise) and it will be *substantially* easier to cut with the grain than across the grain. This gives you an opportunity to test the sharpness of your blade even more. When you can make a *single push cut* in a piece of phone book paper like the one shown in Figure 86, you have a really sharp knife.

Figure 86: A really sharp knife

If your blade is not doing at all well cutting phone book paper, you can try cutting printer paper, which requires a less sharp blade. Then you can work your way up to phone book paper as your sharpening skills improve.

 The Shaving Test

Another common test is to use the knife to shave the hair on your arm. Of course, you can only perform this test a limited number of times per day!

The Fingernail Test

Yet another test is to *carefully* place the blade of the knife *flat* against your fingernail, with the blade pointing toward your hand. The goal is to *slowly* raise the angle that the knife makes with your fingernail while applying *very, very slight forward-only* pressure to see at what angle the knife edge begins to dig into your nail. Be careful! The sharper the blade, the lower the angle at which there is a grab. Personally, I don't care for this test.

 The Hair Whittling Test

Perhaps the ultimate test for sharpness is **hair whittling**. This is a test wherein you hold a loose hair by one end and attempt to whittle the unsupported end. (The hair must be held by the end *opposite* that of the root so that the knife blade can catch the scales of the hair.) Figure 87 shows a micrograph I took of a hair that I whittled after sharpening an inexpensive knife (about $20) freehand, using an Atoma 1200 grit diamond stone, followed by a Spyderco ultra-fine ceramic stone and then a 0.5μ strop. (I will discuss all of these sharpening media in due course.) As you can see from the figure, I was able to whittle this hair several times. This knife is sharp!

Figure 87: My efforts at hair whittling

A test similar to the hair whittling test is the **hanging hair test** used to test the sharpness of straight razors. For more on this test, I refer you to the web site

http://www.coticule.be/hanging-hair-test.html

You can also find a collection of interesting sharpness tests used on razors at

http://straightrazorplace.com/srpwiki/index.php/Sharpness_tests_ex
plained

Feeling for Blade Irregularities

There is another test for blade quality that I hesitate a bit to describe, because it is a bit scary. You can check to see if there are any irregularities such as minute chips or bends in the cutting edge of your blade by running your fingernail along the cutting edge of the blade *as lightly and carefully as possible*, as shown in Figure 88. *Be really careful here!*

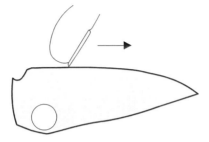

Figure 88: Feeling for irregularities

 # Reasons For Sharpening

There are several reasons for taking your blade to a sharpening stone or system.

 Edge Repair

If you drop a knife or just have the bad luck to cut into a hidden piece of hard metal buried within a softer material, you may chip the cutting edge of the knife. Then you may need to do some serious metal removal in order to remove the chips. This can be a nasty task, depending both on how much metal you need to remove and the hardness of the steel.

Especially if you are relatively new to sharpening, you may consider this task to be either a good learning experience or you may decide, based on how much you love that particular knife (or how much it cost) to let a professional handle the job.

Of course, repairing an edge is more difficult using a freehand approach. If you have a motorized sharpener, such as the Work Sharp, the job will be much easier. An assisted sharpening system will also repair an edge much more easily than a freehand approach, because you can apply a more consistent sharpening force to the blade.

Edge Reprofiling

I have already discussed bevel angles for knife blades and so I won't go into that here. Suffice it to say that edge reprofiling can also be somewhat of a task, especially if you try to do it freehand.

 Sharpening

Of course, most of the time you will simply want to put a sharper edge on a knife that has dulled through use. I will turn to this topic in detail in a moment.

 # Grits and Microns

Buying sharpening stones for either freehand or assisted sharpening is made more complicated by the way in which the abrasiveness of a sharpening stone is measured. Two methods are in common practice.

Particle Size

The first method is abrasive **particle size**, measured in microns, denoted by the Greek letter mu (μ). A **micron** is one millionth of a meter. Today's abrasives range in particle size from about 120μ down to 0.025μ, which is 25 **nanometers** or 25 *billionths* of a meter.

Particle size would seem to be a relatively reliable way to compare the abrasiveness of stones from different companies that use the *same abrasive medium*. However, it is not perfect. For one thing, the characteristics of an abrasive will also depend on the binding medium in which the abrasive is embedded. The more easily the abrasive particles can break free from the binding medium, the less aggressive will be the sharpening action. Also, the *type* of abrasive will have an effect on sharpening action. For example, it seems reasonable to say that diamond particles (Mohs 10) of a given size will cut more quickly than aluminum oxide particles (Mohs 9) of the same size.

Many, but unfortunately not all manufacturers of abrasive materials report abrasiveness in terms of particle size.

Grit Measurement

The other measure of abrasiveness, namely **grit size**, is complicated by the fact that there are several different grit standards, each with its own measuring scale. The U.S. scale is set by **ANSI** (American National Standards Institute), the European scale by **FEPA** (European Federation of Abrasives Producers) and the Japanese scale by **JIS** (Japanese Industrial Standards Organization). To make life even more complicated, for example, ANSI has *two* standards. One standard, named B74.18, is for *coated* abrasives and the other standard, named B74.10, is for *bound* abrasives, such as the stones that I will be discussing.

This sort of gritty chaos makes it difficult to compare the abrasiveness of stones from two different manufacturers. Figure 89 shows a small translation table to help you make comparisons. However, for various reasons, I am skeptical about making comparisons between *different* abrasive materials using either particle size or grits. For example, a new extra-coarse diamond stone rated at 60μ particle size cuts much more aggressively than a new Shapton 220 grit stone rated at 67μ particle size.

Indeed, the only thing I am totally comfortable saying is that, for example, a 20 micron stone is coarser than a 10 micron stone *of the same make and model*, but not necessarily twice as coarse (whatever that might mean)! I will elaborate on the first column of this table later.

Purpose	Microns	Shapton	Chosera	Spyderco	DMT	Atoma
Repair/Reprofile	120–129	120(122μ)			EEC(120μ)	140x(120μ)
Repair/Reprofile	110–119					
Repair/Reprofile	100–109					
Repair/Reprofile	90–99					
Repair/Reprofile	80–89					
Repair/Reprofile	70–79					
Repair/Reprofile	60–69	220(67μ)			EC(60μ)	
Sharpen	50–59					
Sharpen	40–49	320(46μ)			C(45μ)	400x(40μ)
Sharpen	30		400(30μ)			
Sharpen	29	500(29μ)				600x(29μ)
Sharpen	25				F(25μ)	
Sharpen	20		600(20μ)			
Sharpen/Hone	15	1000(14.7μ)		Med(15μ)		
Sharpen/Hone	14		800(14μ)			
Sharpen/Hone	13					1200x(13μ)
Sharpen/Hone	11.5		1000(11.5μ)			
Sharpen/Hone	9				EF(9μ)	
Hone	7	2000(7.35μ)				
Hone	6		2000(6.7μ)	Fine(6μ)		
Hone/Polish	5	3000(4.9μ)				
Polish	3.68	4000(3.68μ)	3000(4μ)			
Polish	3			UF(3μ)	EEF(3μ)	
Polish	2.45	6000(2.45μ)	5000(2.8μ)			
Polish/Ultra Polish	1.84	8000(1.84μ)				
Ultra Polish	1.74	10000(1.74μ)	10000(1.74μ)			
Ultra Polish	0.92	16000(0.92μ)				
Ultra Polish	0.49	30000(0.49μ)				
Ultra Polish	0.025–0.1					

Figure 89:   Grit comparison table (some larger numbers are rounded)
(E = extra, C = coarse, M = medium, F = fine, U = ultra)

If you want more gritty details about grit standards, you can visit the United Abrasives Manufacturer's Association (UAMA). Here is a relevant link:

http://www.uama.org/Abrasives101/101Standards.html

The Sharpening Process

I will refer to the entire process of creating a final edge on a blade as the **refining process**, so as not to overuse the term *sharpening*, which to some people has a very specific meaning that does not encompass the entire refining process. Also, for convenience, I will use the word "stone" to refer to an abrasive stone or an abrasive belt or even a leather strop.

The following discussion applies equally well to freehand sharpening and to assisted or motorized sharpening. In freehand sharpening, the blade is generally passed over the stone, whereas in assisted sharpening, it is the reverse—the stone is passed over the blade. Fortunately, this difference will not affect our discussion of the general refining process.

I like to think of the refinement process as consisting of the following **stages**, some of which are not always needed and some of which are required only in theoretical sharpening:

1) **Repair** or **Reprofile**: When necessary, repairing or reprofiling a blade generally involves removing a *substantial* amount of metal in order to remove any chips or bends in the blade or to change the cutting bevel angle.
2) **Sharpen**: Narrow the apex of the blade as much as possible by removing metal from the cutting bevel.
3) **Hone**: Make the apex of the blade as straight as possible.
4) **Polish**: The purpose of this optional operation is to reduce friction and, of course, to be able to see yourself in the reflection!
5) **Ultra-Polish**: Now that modern technology has provided incredibly fine abrasives (on the order of 25–100 nanometers), I have added this very optional category.

Each pass of the blade over the abrasive (or the abrasive over the blade) will actually sharpen, hone and polish *at the same time*. It is the *level of abrasiveness* that determines how well each of these stages is accomplished with any particular stone. Let me explain this further.

No matter how fine the abrasive, say even as fine as the 0.5 micron particle size that is often used for polishing, rubbing a knife blade against this abrasive (or vice versa) *will* remove some steel from the blade. Just take a look at the abrasive surface of a strop, for example. It will have black marks on it. This is steel removed from the knife blade. Thus, every swipe of the blade sharpens the blade, at least to some extent. However, the final refining steps that use ultra fine abrasives *polish much more and sharpen much less*.

Also, every time you swipe your blade across any abrasive medium (or vice versa), you *will* bend the apex a bit: The direction of the forces involved imply that this must happen. As you move to less abrasive media, you simply bend the edge less, that is, you hone the blade a little better until the generated burr becomes so small that it can no longer be detected and the apex is declared to be straight.

I also choose to say that all stones *polish*. A 500 grit stone simply does a lousy job of polishing—not as lousy as a 250 grit stone—but lousy nonetheless. A shine begins to appear on an edge polished at somewhere around the 2 to 5 micron particle size, but does not really begin to reflect until around the 0.5 to 2 micron particle size. (These are approximate numbers.)

While I believe (as I have just argued) that each pass of the abrasive sharpens, hones and polishes regardless of the level of abrasiveness, it is certainly true that each level of abrasive has a *specific purpose* (with some overlap, of course). For instance, no one would dispute that fact that the purpose of a 120-grit ceramic stone is to repair or reprofile a blade or *maybe* to rough sharpen, but certainly not to hone or polish. A 30000-grit ceramic stone is definitely intended for ultra polishing only.

I included a *rough estimate* as to the purpose of each grit in Figure 89. Figure 90 gives a summary. You will be pleased to know that generally speaking, it is not necessary to purchase more than one stone per category, unless of course you want too.

Purpose	Range (microns)
Repair/Reprofile	60 +
Sharpen	10–60
Hone	5–15
Polish	2 –5
Ultra Polish	0.025–2

Figure 90: Particle size purposes (approximate)

One point I want to emphasize is that the purpose of a stone of a certain particle size also depends on the abrasive used in stone. For example, I consider an extra-coarse diamond stone at 60μ to be a repair/reprofile stone but I will sometimes start my *sharpening* routine with the Shapton 220 grit stone at 67μ.

 ## A Word About Sharpening Angles and Microbevels

Let me make a few comments about bevel angles.

Take Advantage of Higher-Quality Steels

The first point I want to make is that if you purchase a knife with a high-quality steel such as M390 or ZPD-189, you should try to take advantage of the steel's superior ability to hold an edge by sharpening at as small an angle as you are comfortable using. It is true that you run an increased risk of chipping, so the optimal angle may take some experimentation and of course will depend on how you intend to use the knife. My point is this: If you sharpen your ZDP-189 blades at the same angle as your 8Cr13MoV blades, you are probably not taking advantage of the more expensive steel. Just a thought.

The Microbevel

As we have discussed, there are a lot of opinions about the best bevel angle for a given situation. If you are uncertain what bevel angle you want for a particular knife, or maybe even if you are certain, here is an idea that you might want to consider. It was first presented to me by Clay Allison, the inventor of the Wicked Edge sharpening system.

Let us suppose that your knife has a high quality supersteel such as ZDP-189 or Elmax. You guess that such steel might be able to stand up to a 17° cutting bevel, for example. But rather than sharpen the bevel at 17°, you could sharpen at 15° or even 14° and test the edge on some materials that you usually cut? If the edge fails quickly, then you can put a *microbevel* on the blade at a higher angle of 16° or 17°.

A **microbevel** is a tiny bevel at the apex of the blade, as shown in Figure 91.

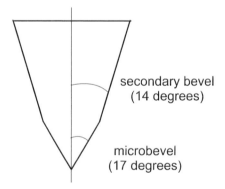

secondary bevel
(14 degrees)

microbevel
(17 degrees)

Figure 91: A microbevel

Microbevels are used frequently in woodworking, in particular on plane blades and bench chisels. The reason is that chisels, for example, have a chisel grind and a very large single bevel, generally made of hard steel. Every time a chisel with no microbevel needs sharpening, you must wear down the entire bevel in order to sharpen the chisel. This is time consuming and wastes precious metal. However, if a microbevel is present, you need only refine that tiny bevel, which takes but a few strokes on a fine stone.

By doing this **microbevel trick** on your knife, you can experiment with different bevel angles until you find the right one for your particular needs. Adding a microbevel, sharpening an existing microbevel or changing the angle of an existing microbevel generally involves only very light work with a sharpening stone or system.

In addition, if you polish the main cutting bevel (as well as the microbevel) to a high polish, you will have a large, shiny bevel with which to impress your friends as well as an edge that should hold up well because the microbevel has been adjusted to extend the life of the edge. Thus, you get *the best of both worlds*, so to speak.

 *Raising a Burr*

Before discussing the individual steps in the refining process, I need to discuss the concept of a *burr*. Rubbing a blade across the surface of an abrasive such as a sharpening stone will bend the apex of the blade, thus producing a **burr** (or **bur**), as shown in Figure 92. This is referred to as **raising a burr** on the cutting edge.

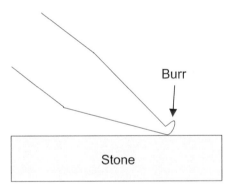

Figure 92: A burr

Figure 93 shows an electron micrograph of a freshly sharpened edge with no significant visible burr.

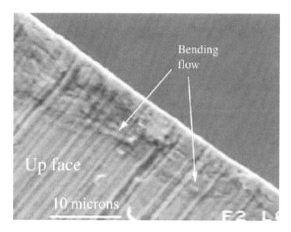

Figure 93: Edge with no burr

Figure 94 shows the other side of the same blade, with a definite burr.

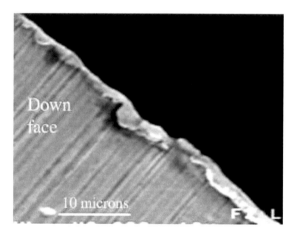

Figure 94: Edge with burr

(Both of these electron micrographs are from Professor John Verhoeven's paper *Experiments on Knife Sharpening*.)

Of course, the burr will point in the direction opposite to the side of the blade that is in contact with the abrasive stone. When you flip the blade and begin to sharpen the other side, you will either break off the burr if you sharpen too aggressively or bend it in the opposite direction. However, you do *not* want to break it off because this will tend to leave a jagged apex (unless of course that is what you want). In general, it is better to *wear down* the burr rather than break it off. Removing the burr is referred to as **deburring**.

Burrs should be *as small as possible* at all times. A burr should generally be felt but not seen (except by reflection in a strong light). At the finer levels of abrasiveness, it will take some practice even to feel a burr. A large burr has no advantage because even the tiniest burr signals that you have reached the apex of the blade. Moreover, a large burr simply means that you have removed more precious metal than necessary. If you can see the burr without optical aid, it is probably too large.

There are three common ways to detect the presence of a burr.

1)   You can feel for a burr using the tip of your finger. It will take some practice to tell when you have achieved the tiniest of burrs.
2)   You can scrape your fingernail off the edge of the blade in the direction *perpendicular* to the cutting edge, as shown in Figure 95.

Figure 95: Scrape down to feel a burr with fingernail

If your fingernail gets snagged ever so slightly at the apex of the blade, you have a burr. I find this to be the most reliable way to detect a fine burr.
3)   If you place the edge under a strong light and move it around, a burr will gleam at you if you can find the right viewing angle.

 The Mechanics of Refining

The concepts of sharpening, honing and polishing are certainly important but also somewhat theoretical. From a *practical* point of view, each step of the refining process has two objectives.

Raising a Burr

One objective is to raise the smallest possible burr along the *entire* cutting edge. In some sense, the presence of a burr means that you have already gone "too far" in the refinement process, but it is literally impossible to stop at a point where the *very next* stroke on the stone would be the *first* stroke to raise a burr. Your goal is to go as little "too far" as possible.

Unfortunately, as the sharpening process moves to the finer abrasives, it becomes harder and harder to detect a burr and you must eventually abandon the idea of wearing down a burr that you cannot detect. At this point, you simply refine both sides of the blade until you feel that the edge is as sharp as you can get it with that particular abrasive. As you proceed, you can test the edge with some phone book paper, for example. Experience will tell you when you are ready to move to the next finer abrasive.

Removing Old Scratch Marks

The second objective concerns the bevel rather than the apex and is to remove the scratch pattern left by the previous stone. For this purpose, I keep a magnifying glass handy. In fact, I like to don a head-mounted magnifying glass (10x) and work under a good light. Then I can very easily inspect the bevel at any time by flipping the magnifying glass down over my eyes.

However, if the two stones are very close in abrasiveness, it is easy to miss a few of the older marks even with a magnifying glass. To mitigate this problem, a useful trick is to use different scratch patterns for successive stones. Here is how it works.

When you come near the end of the refinement process with a particular stone, make your last few strokes using a right-to-left movement (say) in order to impart a right-to-left scratch pattern on the bevel of the knife. Then, you start the next stone with any type of stroke you prefer (left-to-right, up and down, circular, whatever) *except* right-to-left strokes until all of the previous stone's right-to-left scratch marks are gone.

Unfortunately, the two objectives of producing a small burr and removing the scratch marks left by the previous stone are not always in sync, that is, you may arrive at the perfect burr *before* you have removed all of the scratches left by the previous stone (or vice versa). When this happens to me, I continue with the same stone until both objectives are met.

But How To Do it?

It might seem as though the best way to sharpen a blade is to take alternating passes on each side of the blade and *in theory* I agree with this assessment. In this way, you will bend the apex of the blade less than if you take multiple strokes on one side.

The problem with this approach is that it is hard to tell when to move on to the next abrasive. Without the development of a burr, how do you know that you have reached the apex of the blade?

Well, you could check for a burr after *each* pass with the knife, but that is way too tedious for most of us. Alternatively you could make several alternating passes on each side of the blade and then test for sharpness, but this can also be rather tedious. The third alternative is the one most often employed and goes as follows.

1) Refine one side of the blade until you get the smallest possible burr along the entire apex and have removed the previous stone's scratch marks. Pause every few strokes or so to check for a burr.

2) Once this has been achieved on the first side of the blade, repeat the process on the other side of the blade. You also want to ensure that both sides of the blade have an equal-sized cutting bevel, which may require a bit more work on one side than the other.

3) At this point, you have a blade whose bevel has an even scratch pattern characteristic of the current abrasive as well as a small burr bent in one direction. Now you want to **deburr**, that is, you want to *gently* work the burr from side to side in order to wear it down. To move the burr back and forth without increasing its size, take fewer and fewer strokes with lighter and lighter pressure as you alternate sides. Eventually, you will take only one stroke on each side of the blade, letting the weight of the stone supply the sharpening force.

Some Tips

Let me suggest some tips to make the refinement process run more smoothly.

1) As you rub the blade against the stone (or vice versa), *use only light pressure—* let the abrasive cut into the steel—do not force it. Also, as you come to the end with a particular stone, take lighter and lighter strokes.

If you find that you need to use more than light (or *slightly* more than light) pressure to remove the previous stone's scratches, then you may be using the wrong level of abrasiveness, that is, there may be too large a gap between the level of abrasiveness of this stone and the previous stone. As an extreme example, you cannot expect to remove the scratches from a 500 grit stone with an 8000 grit stone.

Herein lies the problem of which stones to buy (for either freehand or assisted sharpening). There is quite a bit of opinion about which stone grit will make a good stone set. You can generally skip levels of abrasiveness when buying a stone set, with the understanding that the larger the gap between stones, the more work you will need to do with the finer stone in order to remove the stone's scratch marks left by the previous coarser stone. As an example, consider the Shapton Glass Stones. Figure 96 shows the grit sizes.

Shapton Grit	Particle Size (Microns)
120	122.5
220	66.82
320	45.94
500	29.4
1000	14.7
2000	7.35
3000	4.9
4000	3.68
6000	2.45
8000	1.84
10000	1.74
16000	0.92
30000	0.49

Figure 96: Shapton grit sizes

Now, it would certainly seem unnecessary to buy both an 8000 (1.84μ) and a 10000 (1.74μ) grit stone since their particle sizes are so close to each other. One possibility is to first decide whether you wanted to start with a 6000 or an 8000 stone and then work your way up, trying to roughly double the particle size along the way. This leads to the following stone sets

6000 (2.45μ), 3000 (4.9μ), 1000 (14.7μ), 500 (29.4μ), 220 (66.82μ)

and perhaps a bit better (but more expensive),

8000 (1.84μ), 4000 (3.86μ), 2000 (7.35μ), 1000 (14.7μ), 500 (29.4μ), 220 (66.82μ)

2) Learn to develop a *feel* for the cutting action of the stone and learn to take heed of the *sound* that the stone makes as it abrades the blade. Every type of stone has a different feel or **feedback** to it, which I suspect is a major reason that some people prefer one type of stone over another type. With some experience, you can tell by feel and sound whether you are sharpening the knife with the stone or cutting the stone with the knife!

3) You may find times as you progress through the different levels of abrasiveness that a certain stone is just not doing what you want it to do. Perhaps you are not getting a decent burr or perhaps you cannot reach all of the scratch marks of the previous stone because of minute "valleys" in the bevel. If this happens, then you will need to back up to the previous level of abrasiveness. You will loose the work you did with the finer stone, but such is life. The point to remember is that refining at a certain grit level generally will not cover up any mistakes or

omissions made at the coarser grits—to fix a problem created (or overlooked) at a coarser grit, you need to use that grit.

Polished But Dull

Another issue that I see with freehand sharpening is that you may complete the entire sharpening process and end up with a beautifully polished but *dull* knife! Let me explain how this can happen.

At an enhanced magnification, a freehand bevel is very unlikely to be a flat plane. It is more likely to look like the multi-faceted bevel in Figure 97.

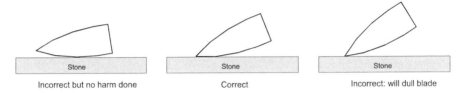

| Incorrect but no harm done | Correct | Incorrect: will dull blade |

Figure 97: Freehand mistakes

Now, if you pass the blade over the stone at too shallow an angle, as on the left in Figure 97, then no harm will be done to the apex—all you will do is create more facets in the cutting bevel, or refine existing facets. However, if you pass the blade over the stone with too steep an angle, as on the right in Figure 97, you will round over the apex of the blade. The trick is to maintain the angle shown in the center of Figure 97. If you consistently wander off this angle by too much, you will get a nicely polished bevel and a dull knife!

I still have this problem from time to time while freehand sharpening. On occasion, I may think that I have finished with a stone, but when I test the edge, it does not cut as expected. Then I simply return the knife to that same stone, take a deep breadth, remember my words here and start over with that stone. In fact, occasionally I need to redo the entire freehand sharpening process.

 Setting the Sharpening Angle—The Sharpie® Trick

If you are sharpening a knife (but not reprofiling it), then you will need to determine the existing sharpening angle for the knife. This applies to sharpening both freehand and with a sharpening system.

Determining the current sharpening angle of your knife requires a bit of ingenuity, because the cutting bevel is so small that it cannot really be measured reliably with any sort of angle gauge. Enter the **Sharpie trick**. The idea is simple and is shown in Figure 98. First, you paint the entire cutting bevel with a black Sharpie (or similar marker). Then you *estimate* the correct sharpening angle and take one *very light* swipe with (or on) the sharpening stone. The location of the ink that is removed will indicate whether you have found the correct angle or whether the setting is too high or too low. You may want to swipe at several locations along the edge. If you find that the angle setting is correct at one location but not at another location, you will need to decide what angle provides a good compromise so you don't need to remove too much metal from any portion of the edge. Also, I suggest that you use a very fine stone for this procedure, sothat in case your setting is too high, you will not round over the apex of the blade significantly.

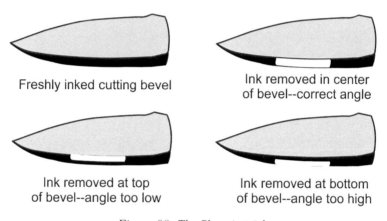

Freshly inked cutting bevel

Ink removed in center
of bevel--correct angle

Ink removed at top
of bevel--angle too low

Ink removed at bottom
of bevel--angle too high

Figure 98: The Sharpie trick

 ## *Reestablishing The Angle*

Of course, the Sharpie trick is not of much use in freehand sharpening unless you can duplicate the angle each time you swipe the knife. As I have said, this is the main issue in freehand sharpening.

I must admit that when I first started freehand sharpening, I was incredulous. It just didn't seem possible to consistently establish the same angle over and over again by hand. Nevertheless freehand sharpening does work. I think it is a combination of two things: Our fingers (really our brains) are more sensitive to reestablishing angles than I thought and reestablishing the *exact* same angle is not as important as I thought.

My first several attempts at freehand sharpening were dismal failures, but the more I practiced, the better I got, until one day it just worked. Now I can usually get as sharp an edge on a knife by freehand sharpening as I can with a sharpening system. When I do fail to get the results I want, I just back up and redo some of the steps until I do. Even with some backing up, the freehand process is often faster than using a sharpening system.

If you want to watch some excellent YouTube videos on freehand sharpening, I suggest the following links

https://www.youtube.com/watch?v=ZsLaTtrSEj0

and

https://www.youtube.com/watch?v=Kc1bdN2ELSs

The Work Sharp Guided Sharpening System

The advantage of using a sharpening system with guides is that you will probably get good results much more quickly and with much less frustration than sharpening freehand. However, if you like the idea of doing freehand sharpening but want a little help at the beginning, Work Sharp has just come out with an excellent product just for you. It is called the **Work Sharp Guided Sharpening System**. This guide is pictured in Figure 99.

Figure 99: The Guided Sharpening System

The idea of the device is quite simple. You first install the appropriate angle ramps at the ends of the device. In the figure, the 20° ramps are snapped in place. Then you install the abrasive stone of the desired grit. To sharpen freehand, place the knife blade on the angle ramp to set the angle. Then carefully move the knife to the stone and get to work. Any time you feel you may have drifted off the sharpening angle, you can easily reestablish the angle by placing the knife blade back on the angle ramp. This solidly-built system provides "training wheels" for freehand sharpening.

The system comes with a fine and a coarse diamond plate, two 17°/20° angle guides and a ceramic honing rod that can be put in place of the diamond stones. The Guided Sharpening System is priced at $59.99. An upgrade kit is available that includes a 25° guide, an extra coarse diamond plate, an extra fine diamond plate and a leather plate, along with stropping compound. The upgrade kit is $34.99.

Sharpening Stones

Now let's discuss sharpening stones and their concomitant paraphernalia. First, let me mention that if you want to delve more deeply into sharpening stones and other related matters, then Tom Blodgett's blog at **Jende Industries'** web site

www.jendeindustries.com

makes very interesting reading. Tom is an expert in sharpening materials. He also sells a wide variety of sharpening supplies.

Abrasive stones used for sharpening folding knifes generally come in sizes ranging from 2x6 inches to 3x10 inches. I find the 3x8 inch size to be ideal for my folding knives. The thickness of these stones can vary from, say 1/2-inch to perhaps 3 inches.

 Flatness

One important aspect of sharpening stones is their flatness. In the woodworking word, this is a critical issue. Woodworkers expect their plane blades, for example, to be able to shave off uniform ribbons of wood on the order of one thousandth of an inch thick and so these blades must be dead flat (and dead sharp!). Consequently, the stones used to sharpen plane blades must also be dead flat.

For sharpening knifes, flatness is not quite as critical. Still, sharpening is hard enough without worrying about whether or not the flatness of your stones is having an effect on the results. Therefore, I prefer to use stones that are not more than a thousandth of an inch or so out of flat.

One of the advantages of the softer sharpening stones is that they can be flattened with a diamond flattening plate and thereby brought to this level of flatness. (More on this later.) However, diamond stones and the harder ceramic stones cannot be flattened and so we are at the mercy of manufacturing tolerances in these cases. If you decide to purchase stones that cannot be flattened, it would probably be a good idea to make sure you can return them should they be too far out of flat. A high-quality straight edge and feeler gauges can be used to check for flatness.

Types of Sharpening Stones

Most sharpening stones fall into one of two broad categories: *diamond stones* and *ceramic stones*.

Diamond Stones

Diamond stones consist of industrial diamond chips embedded in a nickel plating on the surface of a steel plate. They are generally used with a small amount of water as lubricant. Diamond stones tend to be the most expensive sharpening stones.

Ceramic Stones

The term *ceramic* applies to a wide variety of chemical substances but the term **ceramic stone** is generally used in the sharpening world to refer to stones whose abrasive material is either aluminum oxide or silicon carbide. Since silicon carbide is harder than aluminum oxide, the former abrasive tends to be used more often in the coarser stones and can often be detected by its green color. Aluminum oxide stones are often pure white or have been artificially colored in order to easily distinguish grit size. These abrasives are bound into a stone shape using a **binding agent**.

Binding agents can vary quite a bit in firmness. When the binding agent is very firm, the stone is so hard that wear is relatively insignificant, but flattening is not possible by ordinary means. Ceramic stones with softer binding agents will wear significantly but will also require regular flattening. (Again, more on this later.)

The softer ceramic stones are said to be **renewable** because they expose fresh layers of abrasive as they wear. Of course, diamond stones and the harder ceramic stones are not renewable.

Some say that the softer stones cut more aggressively because they are constantly exposing fresh abrasive material as they wear. I think this is true for high-quality stones, such as the ones I am discussing. However, taken to the extreme, if the abrasive material were bound in wet mud, I doubt that the stone would cut anything. Therefore, there must be some point at which the softness of the binding agent becomes counterproductive to the sharpening process. Put another way, if the abrasive is held too loosely in the binding medium, then it will be more-or-less pushed out of the way by the knife blade.

We have seen that the firmness of the binding affects the overall firmness of the stone. However, there is another aspect to the firmness of sharpening stones. Specifically, among a given line of ceramic stones (such as Shapton or Chosera) the coarser stones are more **friable** (easily crumbled) and more porous and therefore require more frequent flattening than the finer stones.

Common Abrasive Stones

The most common abrasive stones in the knife world (as far as I know) are

- Oil stones
- Traditional Japanese waterstones (natural and synthetic)
- Shapton Glass and Professional stones
- Naniwa Chosera stones
- Edge Pro stones
- Spyderco stones
- DMT and Atoma diamond stones

All of these stones are ceramic except the diamond stones.

 ## *Cutting Characteristics of Abrasive Stones*

There are several parameters that give an abrasive stone its cutting characteristics. Some of these parameters are

- the hardness of the abrasive itself,
- the shapes and sizes of the abrasive particles,
- the distribution of the particles within the binding medium (random or purposely arranged)
- the hardness of the binding medium in which the abrasive particles are held.

All these parameters contribute to the speed at which the different stones cut as well as the surface that they leave in the metal. As Tom Blodgett puts it very succinctly in his blog "When you start mixing in the effects of the different abrasives, their shapes, and a stone's binders and matrices, things quickly get complicated."

 ## *Slurry and Swarf*

But life is even more complicated than that. As you rub a knife blade against an abrasive stone, the abrasive particles will break off to varying degrees depending on the abrasive material. The resulting paste-like substance is called **slurry**.

Along with slurry, metal from the blade is also being deposited on the stone's surface. This mixture of loose particles of metal and lubricant (oil or water) is called **swarf**. Thus, as you continue to sharpen, both slurry and swarf combine to make a dark-colored mud-like concoction on the stone.

Not being a material scientist or a physicist, I cannot speak authoritatively about the relative effects of this concoction on the sharpening process. Some say that the presence of slurry can *speed up* the cutting process because the density of abrasive particles is higher in the slurry than in the stone. On the other hand, some say that the presence of slurry can *slow down* the cutting process because the loose slurry insulates the knife a bit from the stone itself and the loose particles of abrasive just get pushed out of the way by the knife. I have also heard it said that the presence of slurry tends to make the cutting action smoother, as though the stone was of a finer grit. These are issues that you can certainly decide for yourself with a little experience.

The relative amounts of slurry and swarf in the mud, and therefore the effect of this mud on sharpening, depend on the type of abrasive and the type of binder. A *broken-in* diamond stone creates less slurry and more swarf than the other stones. Note, however, that diamonds will break off from a new stone more than one might think. Put another way, diamond stones do have a break-in period during which the looser/larger diamond particles will abrade away.

Lubricants

The purpose of a **lubricant** is to prevent the slurry/swarf mud from sticking to or becoming embedded in the stone. Of course, oil stones use oil as a lubricant and waterstones use water. The ceramic stones like Shapton and Chosera stones also use water. The coarser stones require more water than the finer stones, because they absorb more water.

I believe that the Spyderco ceramic stones and diamond stones should be used with a small amount of water to float the swarf/slurry. I also like to occasionally use the Trend diamond abrasive lapping fluid with my continuous diamond stones.

Stone Holders

In order to use a sharpening stone for freehand sharpening, you will need some sort of platform or **stone holder** on which to hold the stone in place and to raise it to a convenient height off the table to make room for your knuckles, which will fall below the level of the stone.

Figure 100: Stone holders (Shapton on left)

Shapton sells a beautiful, heavy glass stone holder for their stones, which I like a lot (on the left in Figure 100). It can be used with other stones of the same size (or smaller by using wedges to hold the stone in place. However, this stone holder costs over a hundred dollars!

On the other hand, if you search for "sharpening stone holder" on Amazon, you will find some adjustable options in the $20 range (on the right in Figure 100).

Perhaps the best alternative is simply to build your own wooden platform out of plywood or MDF, attach some rubber feet to the bottom and cover the top with, say, duck tape to protect it from the water or oil lubricant.

Flattening Stones

As I discussed earlier, all but the hardest ceramic stones will wear and will require regular flattening. Just how often they require flattening depends both on their softness and on how you use the stones. When sharpening woodworking chisels and plane blades, I will sometimes pause to flatten a stone *during a single sharpening operation*, but for knives, this is probably not necessary, unless you cut a gouge into one of the stones by accident. To flatten a stone, you will need an abrasive that is both flat and more aggressive than the stone you are flattening.

There are several options when it comes to a **flattening stone**, also called a **truing stone** or **lapping plate**.

Diamond Lapping Plate

The best but (naturally) the most expensive method is to use a **diamond flattening stone**. The Shapton diamond flattening stone costs a whopping $380! Also, it is *not* recommended for the coarsest of ceramic stones—nothing over 500 grit. DMT makes a **diamond lapping plate** that sells for about $180 on Amazon.

You can also flatten the Japanese waterstones, the Shapton stones and the Chosera stones with regular diamond stones, instead of a special-purpose diamond lapping plate. However, you don't want the difference in grits between the flattening stone and the target stone to be too great or you will leave a very rough texture on the surface of the target stone. For instance, you do not want to flatten an 8000 grit Shapton with an extra-extra coarse diamond stone. This causes no permanent damage and can be removed with a finer lapping stone, but will waste material.

If you look on the Jende Industries web site under Atoma diamond stones, you will find some recommendations as follows:

- The #140 diamond stone (100μ particle size) can lap stones from 120 grit and higher [finer].

- The #400 diamond stone (45μ particle size) can lap stones from 400 grit and finer.
- The #600 diamond stone (29μ particle size) can lap stones from 2000 grit and finer.
- The #1200 diamond stone (15μ particle size) can lap stones from 5000 grit and finer.

Just some guidelines.

Sandpaper on a Flat Surface

Another alternative for flattening is to use sandpaper on a flat surface, such as MDF (medium density fiberboard) or float glass. Also, Woodcraft sells a *very flat* granite plate for about $40, which would be an excellent bed for the sandpaper. However, the breakoff from the stones will clog the sandpaper fairly quickly, so using sandpaper is not an ideal solution. You will need to flatten *very often* with this system, so that you only need to remove a small amount of abrasive. In fact, eventually, you will end up spending more money on sandpaper than the price of a diamond flattening stone, and have a lot less joy in the meantime.

Flattening Stones for Japanese Waterstones

Both Norton and Naniwa make flatting stones for waterstones, available on Amazon for about $30. I have not used either of these so I cannot attest to their efficacy. (My main concern would be their flatness.) However, since most other ceramic stones are much harder than waterstones, these flatteners may very well not be suitable for the Shapton, Chosera or Edge Pro stones. (Let me know if you try it.)

Abrasive Powder on Glass

Yet another alternative is to use silicon carbide (or aluminum oxide) powder on a glass plate. This is the solution recommended by Edge Pro for their stones, which I will discuss later. However, the Edge Pro stones are much harder than the Shapton or Chosera stones (Ben Dale, the inventor of the edge Pro says five times harder) and I would be very concerned about using an abrasive powder on the softer stones, because the powder could easily get embedded in the stone—a *very* bad scene.

Flattening, Yuck!

Flattening is definitely the bane of sharpening. However, you should not ignore this expensive issue. I have heard several sharpening experts say that the *second* stone you buy should be a flattening stone!

Technique

As to technique, the main tip you need when flattening is to use a pencil to place a few scribble marks over *every* section of the stone to be flattened. Then you rub the flattening stone over the stone to be flattened, using light to moderate pressure at different angles and with some lubricant until all of the pencil marks are gone. Then you have a flat stone.

Now let me talk about the stones themselves.

 ## Oil Stones

Oil stones are traditional Western sharpening stones that cut using an embedded abrasive such as aluminum oxide or silicon carbide. The abrasive particles in a **hard Arkansas stone** are more densely packed than in a **soft Arkansas stone** and so the hard stone cuts more finely than the soft stone. The purpose of the oil lubricant is to prevent the swarf from sticking to and becoming embedded in the stone.

I must confess to having very little experience with oil stones. I used them for a short period of time when I started sharpening 30 years ago, but moved quickly to Japanese waterstones for reasons that now escape me.

 ## Traditional Japanese Waterstones

There are two types of traditional **Japanese waterstones**: natural and synthetic. The natural stones are quite a bit more expensive and more rare than the synthetic stones. Natural stones use ash as an abrasive and synthetic stones use either silicon carbide or aluminum oxide. The binder in a Japanese waterstone is a relatively soft material (such as clay) which makes the stones more friable than the other stones I am discussing.

As a result, Japanese water stones cut more quickly than oil stones, which is generally a good thing, but they also wear more quickly, which is a bad thing, because they need flattening more often.

The coarser grits of waterstones soak up a lot of water and may need to be soaked in water before use. The finer grits should work fine with just a spritzing of water. One disadvantage to using water as a lubricant is that it promotes rust, so scrupulous drying and light oiling of your blades are required after sharpening.

Traditional Japanese water stones come in a variety of grits from 120 to 10000. I have not used traditional Japanese waterstones for many years (decades, in fact), so I cannot speak with any authority about how modern Japanese waterstones perform with today's *very hard* knife supersteels. Personally, I would be very cautious about investing in a complete set of these stones until I did further investigation. At the very least, I would buy one of the coarser stones and try it out.

 ## Shapton Glass Ceramic Stones

Shapton Glass Stones contain aluminum oxide particles that are embedded in a firm medium and bonded to a flat glass plate. Water is used as a lubricant. These stones cut very quickly, are much harder and therefore stay flatter longer than traditional

Japanese waterstones and have excellent feedback, in my opinion. Flattening these stones is more difficult than flattening traditional waterstones. A diamond flattening plate of some kind is probably a must.

I have used Shapton Glass Stones for sharpening knives and woodworking tools for more than a decade and I like them a lot. They can be expensive, however. I checked pricing as of the writing of this book. The 120 grit stone costs about $50 and the price climbs slowly to $140 for the 16000 grit stone. Then 30000 grit stone is a real luxury at $360! Fortunately, it is not needed. In fact, I do not own the 30000-grit stone and I often do not use my 16000-grit stone.

If you are interested in the Shapton stones, there are some videos by Harrelson Stanley on Shapton's web site at

www.shapton.com

Shapton Glass Stones are available in the grits shown in Figure 101, which is a portion of the table in Figure 89.

Purpose	Shapton Grit	Particle Size (Microns)
Repair/Reprofile	120	122.5
Repair/Reprofile	220	66.82
Sharpen	320	45.94
Sharpen	500	29.4
Sharpen/Hone	1000	14.7
Hone	2000	7.35
Hone/Polish	3000	4.9
Polish	4000	3.68
Polish	6000	2.45
Polish/Ultra Polish	8000	1.84
Ultra Polish	10000	1.74
Ultra Polish	16000	0.92
Ultra Polish	30000	0.49

Figure 101: Shapton Glass Stones

 Shapton Professional Stones

Shapton also makes a line of Professional stones that are apparently quite similar in performance to the Glass Stones. I have not used the Professional Stones so I cannot comment about the differences from first hand experience. However, as usual, each product has its advocates.

I must admit to some confusion here, which no one I have spoken to has been able to clear up satisfactorily. The issue revolves around the fact that the Glass Stones have 5mm of abrasive bound to a glass plate whereas the Professional stones (also called the Traditional stones) have three times as much abrasive with no glass backing.

Frankly, since the Glass Stones are more expensive than the Professional stones, I feel like I am missing a piece of the puzzle. Perhaps someone in Japan could spill the beans about the real difference between the stones. The Shapton web site is of no help in this regard (at least not that I have been able to discover). Saying that the two brands are very similar makes me wonder why I paid more for one-third as much abrasive. Does the glass back do something important or just look pretty? On the other hand, in the many years I have owned a full set of the Glass Stones, I have yet to wear out a single stone, so I don't really need the extra abrasive. Oh well, I am quite happy with my Glass Stones so I don't lose any sleep over it.

Naniwa Chosera Stones

Naniwa Chosera (or simply **Chosera**) stones are Japanese aluminum oxide ceramic sharpening stones that are manufactured with a special bonding that allows for greater density and greater consistency in the dispersal of the abrasive particles (or so the company says).

There is much discussion on the Web comparing the Chosera stones and the Shapton stones. I have not spent a lot of time reading these comparisons, but what I have observed is that both stones seem to have a great many advocates, so it appears that this comes down (again) to personal preference. I use them both and would frankly be quite happy with either set. The only concrete difference I observe is that there are a wider range of grits available for the Shapton stones, both on the coarse and on the ultra-fine end.

For a further look at the Chosera and Shapton stones, you might want to visit Tom Blodgett's blog article at

> https://jendeindustries.wordpress.com/2011/03/22/guide-to-using-wicked-edge-weps-chosera-and-shapton-stones/

Tom also has produced an interesting video that discusses how to flatten Chosera and Shapton stones using diamond stones, located at

> https://www.youtube.com/watch?v=XVNFEAiMjzU

Figure 102 shows the available Chosera stones.

Purpose	Chosera Number	Particle Size (Microns)
Sharpen	400	30
Sharpen	600	20
Sharpen/Hone	800	14
Sharpen/Hone	1000	11.5
Hone	2000	6.7
Polish	3000	4
Polish	5000	2.8
Ultra Polish	10000	1.74

Figure 102: Chosera stone grit/particle size

Spyderco Ceramic Stones

Spyderco makes a family of aluminum oxide ceramic stones that are so hard that they do not need to be (nor can they be) flattened. They come in medium, fine and ultra fine, which is a welcome relief from the pressures of deciding which grits to buy. The stones can be used dry or with a small amount of water, which I prefer. The water does not soak into the stone, unlike with the Shapton or Choseras stones, so only a small amount is required.

As I will discuss later, I use the ultra fine ceramic stone (3μ) following the ultra-fine diamond stone (9μ) when sharpening freehand with diamond stones. I also use these stones (or diamond stones) to sharpen carving tools, because the curved edges can easily cut a groove in softer stones.

Unfortunately, I have found that some of these stones are dead flat while others are not. The company says that while they endeavor to make their stones flat, things happen (like warping) and they do not obsess over the issue. This is not so much a problem with knifes as long as the stone is reasonably flat, but it can be a problem with woodworking tools (chisels and plane blades), as I mentioned earlier.

Figure 103 shows the particle size of the Spyderco ceramic stones.

Purpose	Spyderco Stone	Particle Size (Microns)
Sharpen/Hone	Medium	15
Hone/Polish	Fine	6
Polish	Ultra fine	3

Figure 103: Spyderco ceramic stone grit sizes

 *Diamond Stones*

Manmade nano materials aside and Lonsdaleite and wurzite boron nitride notwithstanding, diamond is the hardest known substance and so it should be no surprise that diamond stones cut more quickly and wear more slowly than other stones. Also, they do not require flattening.

As I will discuss a bit later, these are my choice for repairing, reprofiling and sharpening. Unfortunately, diamond stones do not seem to be suitable for polishing however. (More on that in a moment.)

I am familiar with the products of two companies that make diamond stones: **DMT** and **Atoma**, although there are other companies that make diamond stones. The DMT stones use a more-or-less random distribution of diamond particles and the Atoma stones, which are generally more expensive, use a consistent grouping pattern. As usual, when there are two or more similar products with the same intended purpose, there is debate as to which product is superior. Personally, I don't think that either one is superior to the other—they are just different.

For more details and to view lovely micrographs of the scratch patterns left by these stones, I recommend Tom Blodgett's article at

> https://jendeindustries.wordpress.com/2011/09/25/dmt-vs-atoma-diamond-plates-for-the-edge-pro-a-microscopic-comparison

The DMT stones come in different flavors and I prefer the continuous Dia-Sharp stones for knife sharpening. The 8x3-inch stones come in extra-extra coarse, extra-coarse, coarse, fine, extra-fine and extra-extra-fine. However, I find very little use for the extra-extra coarse stone and only occasional use for the extra-coarse stone.

Also, the extra-extra fine stone has been a *big* disappointment to me. It is reported to be a 3 micron stone and so I expected it to leave a close-to-polished finish on my blades. However, even though the stone itself feels *much* smoother than the extra-fine stone, it leaves a finish more like the fine stone! I have spoken several times to the company. They told me that the stone needs breaking in, suggested I use it aggressively for a few hours. I did so, but it did not seem to help. I have sent the stone back to DMT and await their verdict.

As I mentioned earlier, diamond stones do take some time to break in and their aggressiveness will diminish over time. There are several reasons for this. For example, inevitably some of the diamond chips that are not bound as tightly to the underlying medium will slough off the stone with its first few uses. Also, a portion of some of the larger, more irregular shaped diamond chips will break off with use.

However, the stone will "settle in" as time goes on. The most important thing I can say about diamond stones in this regard is the following:

> The secret to getting the longest possible life out of diamond stones is to use LIGHT pressure and let the diamonds do the cutting. Also, it is important to keep your diamond stones clean and store them dry, for they are prone to rusting.

You can use a common kitchen cleanser and a brush to clean a dirty diamond stone.

For reference, Figure 104 shows the particle sizes of the Atoma and DMT diamond stones.

Purpose	Particle Size (Microns)	Atoma	DMT
Repair/Reprofile	120		Extra-extra coarse
Repair/Reprofile	100	140x	
Repair/Reprofile	60		Extra coarse
Sharpen	45	400x	Coarse
Sharpen	29	600x	
Sharpen	25		Fine
Sharpen/Hone	15	1200x	
Hone	9		Extra fine
Hone/Polish	3		Extra-extra fine

Figure 104: DMT diamond stone particle sizes

More Details

My thanks to Dr. Donald Zipperian, a metallurgist with Pace Technologies (www.metallographic.com), who helped me sort out some of the more confusing points (sorry) about diamond abrasives.

The subject of diamond abrasives is actually quite complex. For example, if you poke around the Internet, you will find the terms *monocrystalline* and *polycrystalline*. Unfortunately, it is not easy to get the straight dope on the differences between these two types of crystals as it relates to knife sharpening. It seems that companies that sell just one of these types of diamond crystals claim that the type they sell is superior. (Big surprise, huh?)

Let me try to explain the differences and their consequences, as they have been related to me by various authoritative sources. Figure 105 shows both types of crystals.

Monocrystalline blocky diamond

Polycrystalline multi-faceted diamond

Figure 105: Monocrystalline and Polycrystalline diamonds
(Courtesy of Donald Zipperian)

Monocrystalline diamond crystals are solid crystals that have a more-or-less symmetric shape, resembling cubes with their corners flattened into faces. This shape is called **cubo-octohedral**, and is pictured in Figure 106.

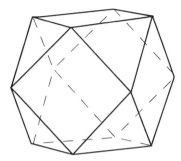

Figure 106: The monocrystalline diamond shape—a cubo-octohedron

As the points on a cubo-octohedral crystal wear down and become flattened, the crystal becomes more and more spherical in shape, thus reducing its aggressiveness. This is the main reason for the breaking-in process that I mentioned earlier. Some refer to this process as *plateauing*.

Polycrystalline diamond crystals are man-made crystals consisting of numerous tiny crystallites that are fused together. This provides a large number of small cutting edges, resulting in a high rate of material removal, while producing only a shallow scratch pattern. The reason is that with use, pieces of the fused crystal will break off, providing new sharp edges. Thus, polycrystalline diamonds are in a sense "self-sharpening" and so they tend to cut more aggressively and last longer than monocrystalline diamonds. Of course, how much longer they will last is not clear.

Dr. Zipperian feels that polycrystalline diamonds are superior at the level of roughly 9 microns and below, but at the coarser levels, the difference is not that significant. Polycrystalline diamonds are also more expensive than monocrystalline diamonds.

If you want to read more about the advantages of polycrystalline diamonds, I suggest the article by Dr. Zipperian at

> http://www.metallographic.com/Newsletters/PC-diamond-newsletter3.PDF

Personally, I cannot say which type of crystal is more suited to knife sharpening. The fact that monocrystalline diamonds wear more quickly than polycrystalline diamonds may not necessarily be a bad thing. It may be that monocrystals are better at the coarser end and polycrystals are better at the finer end. I have not been able to make direct comparisons, since as far as I know all of the available diamond stones are monocrystalline. However, at the lower levels of abrasiveness where diamond pastes and diamond emulsions are available, you do have some choice between monocrystalline products and polycrystalline products.

My Diamond–Ceramic Grit Path

You may have noticed that I have not been shy about giving you my opinion on certain matters. Here is another one.

Personally, I much prefer using diamond stones rather than ceramic stones for repairing, reprofiling and the coarser stages of sharpening. To my mind, the diamond stones cut more quickly and wear more slowly. Moreover, they do not need flattening, which is a huge benefit. Even if you must still invest in a flattening stone for your finer-grit stones, not having to use it for your coarser-grit stones (which need flattening more often than the finer stones) is a big advantage.

Another reason for preferring diamond stones over ceramics when freehand sharpening is that the fewer strokes you need to take, the less likely you are to make a mistake!

When I sharpen freehand, I progress through two or three diamond stones, followed by an ultra-fine *hard* ceramic and then a strop (more on stropping later in the book). It may not be everyone's idea of the best approach to freehand sharpening, but I like it.

So, here is my freehand abrasive path:

1) 45μ DMT or Atoma diamond stone *if necessary*
2) 25μ DMT or 29μ Atoma diamond stone
3) 9μ DMT or 19μ Atoma diamond stone
4) 3μ Spyderco ceramic stone
5) 0.5μ chromium oxide strop
6) 0.1μ diamond emulsion strop (for theoretical sharpening)

For assisted sharpening on any of the systems I will discuss shortly, I do a similar progression from diamond stones to ceramics, but use Edge Pro, Shapton or Chosera stones to bridge the gap between the extra-fine diamond stones and the strop. I will go into more detail when I discuss the individual sharpening systems.

Let me emphasize that there is absolutely nothing wrong with going "all-ceramic," from the coarse stones down to the ultra-fine stones. I am just saying that in my opinion, it involves more work (more sharpening strokes and also more flattening duties) and is generally not my preference, although I do use that path occasionally.

 Sharpening Systems

There are several fine sharpening systems on the market today. I have experience with the following systems:

1)   Edge Pro
2)   KME
3)   Wicked Edge
4)   Work Sharp

and so I will confine my attention to these systems. The Edge Pro, KME and Wicked Edge are all similar in that they are assisted but not motorized. With these systems, you hold (Edge Pro) or clamp (KME and Wicked Edge) the knife and move the stone over the blade, guided by an arm that maintains the same sharpening angle despite your best efforts to change that angle.

The Work Sharp is a motorized system and so has quite a different character from the other systems. It too has a guide to keep you on the straight and narrow, or it can be used freehand.

If after reading this chapter, any of these systems catch your fancy, I strongly suggest that you check out the videos on the company's web site and on YouTube.

 ## *The Edge Pro*

The **Edge Pro** (www.edgeproinc.com) comes in two flavors: the Apex model (shown in Figure 107) and the Professional model. Unless you expect to become a professional sharpener or need the extra features of the Professional model (such as a chisel attachment), I recommend the Apex model, which is considerably less expensive. Both models are solid machines, made from high-quality parts.

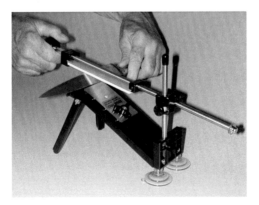

Figure 107: The Edge Pro Apex

As you can glean from Figure 107, the idea of the Edge Pro is quite simple.

1) First, you set the sharpening angle by raising or lowering the block (on the right in the figure) through which the horizontal stone arm slides. There are marks on the vertical rod to help set this angle.
2) Then, you lock a 1x6 inch sharpening stone into the clamp on the stone arm.
3) Next, you place the knife on the table with the cutting edge hanging slightly over the front edge of the table. An adjustable metal plate keeps the knife from sliding down the table. (Some painter's tape on the table under the blade prevents any possible scratches to the blade.)
4) Now you can rub the stone to and fro over the cutting bevel of the knife and the angle will remain constant at each point on the blade.

You can take long, smooth strokes to cover the entire bevel, assuming the knife is not too long or you can "scrub" the edge with the stone. If you scrub, however, you need to be careful to maintain an even bevel along the entire edge. Scrubbing should generally be followed by several long strokes to smooth out any flats, which can usually be seen by moving the blade around under a light.

As long as you do not tip the knife, the angle between the stone and knife will remain constant as you sharpen. You can also slide the knife from left to right to keep the sharpening action directly over the table, but for most folders, this is not necessary. It may be required, however, with very long knives.

Keeping the blade motionless on the table is easy if the blade has a large enough flat spot along the spine or a large ricasso. However, if the blade has a swedge or a small flat along the spine, it can be a bit more difficult, since the blade may rock forward and backward on the table. Then you will need to decide at what orientation you can best hold the knife immobile while operating the stone arm. It may be best to rest the knife on its primary (non cutting) bevel, rather than on a small flat along the spine. In this way, you do not need to fight the (albeit small) force that is applied to the blade by the stone. In any case, you practice is needed to get the hang of how to hold the knife.

The Edge Pro Apex is available in several kits that include sharpening stones and a carrying case (and a few other goodies). I do not think that the two kits (Apex 1 and Apex 2) come with enough stones to do a proper job on your folding knives. The most complete kit is the Apex 4 kit, which is priced at $255. This kit comes with 120, 220, 400, 600 and 1000 grit stones as well as 2000 (9μ particle size) and 3000 (3μ particle size) grit polishing tapes. This and a strop is all that you will need for a professional sharpening job.

The Edge Pro sharpener does not use a clamp to hold the blade in place, unlike the KME and Wicked Edge sharpeners. Some would say this is an advantage and others would say it is a disadvantage. One advantage is that you can easily raise the knife to your eyes to examine the bevel or test its sharpness at any time. Another advantage is that you can slide the knife horizontally along the table in order to avoid swinging the stone arm too far to either side, thus changing the sharpening angle. (More on this later.)

The disadvantages are that you need to keep the knife flat against the table and not let it rock, as I have already discussed. Another issue to consider is that since you must reverse the knife to refine the opposite edge, you will be alternating hands for holding the knife and moving the stone. If you are not *relatively* symmetrically coordinated, one side of the knife could be a bit more awkward to refine than the other. For myself, I am more comfortable holding the knife in my left hand and moving the arm with my right hand, but not so much as to cause any real problems with the opposite hand configuration. (My slight asymmetry causes me some minor problems with the Wicked Edge sharpener as well, but it is not an issue with the KME.)

Which Stones To Use

The ceramic stones that come with the Edge Pro are a little different than the Chosera, Shapton and Spyderco stones that I have already discussed. The abrasive is aluminum oxide (except for the 120-grit stone, which is silicon carbide) as it is for the other stones. On the other hand, the binding is much harder than that found in the Chosera and Shapton stones and yet softer than that of the Spyderco stones. The hardness implies that the stone will stay flat longer and wear less than the Chosera or Shapton stones. However, these stones do need flattening, unlike the Spyderco stones. Diamond stones are *not* recommended for flattening the Edge Pro stones. Instead, Edge Pro recommends silicon carbide powder on glass. (There is a video demonstration of the flattening process on Edge Pro's web site.) Actually, this is not a bad thing, because silicon powder and lapping glass, while a bit messy are significantly cheaper than a diamond flattening plate. (Edge Pro's stone leveling kit is currently priced at $48.)

An alternative to using the Edge Pro stones is to use Atoma diamond, Shapton or Chosera stones, all of which are available in the standard 1x6 inch size. Personally, I like the Atoma stones quite a lot. Incidentally, diamond stones are available from Edge Pro, but the company recommends them for use *only* with ceramic knives.

 *KME Sharpener*

The **KME sharpener** (www.kmesharp.com) is pictured in Figure 108.

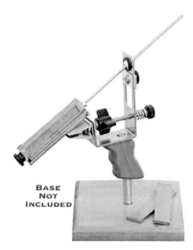

Figure 108: The KME sharpener

This system uses a clamp to hold the knife in position. (There is no knife in the pciture.) As with the Edge Pro, the sharpening stone is held captive and the stone can be moved hither and thither over the knife's edge.

The knife clamp has some advantages over a simple table upon which to hold the knife. The big advantage is stability—you don't need to worry about how you are holding the knife. Another very nice feature of this clamp on the KME is that it rotates 180 degrees (actually 360 degrees) so you can sharpen both sides of the blade very easily and with the same hand orientation.

But the clamping system also has some disadvantages. Foremost is the fact that knives with irregular or tip-to-ricasso tapered blades may not be held securely in the clamp. Some tape or moleskin–like material will generally solve the problem but you *may* encounter a knife that simply cannot be sharpened with a clamp-based sharpening system, although it could also present some problems for the same reason on the Edge Pro.

The clamp is not designed to act like a vice and the farther away from the clamp you make contact with the blade, the more rotational torque you place on the clamp. Fortunately, the KME sharpener has a tension adjustment to help prevent inadvertent rotation. Even if the clamp does not rotate however, it is a bit harder to keep an even stone pressure throughout the entire bevel of a long knife. With the Edge Pro, you can simply slide the knife from left to right to center the region that is being refined.

The KME is a much smaller and lighter machine than the Edge Pro, which also has its advantages and disadvantages. The biggest advantage I find is that you can hold the entire machine (sans base) in your recessive hand and operate the rod/stone assembly with your dominant hand. I like to don my 10x magnifying headband and hold the unit close to my head so I can see how the edge refinement is progressing. I really enjoy watching the sharpening progress in detail. It also makes it much easier to find spots on the edge that need a bit more attention.

Being a smaller unit, the KME uses 4 inch stones, whereas the other models use longer stones. The longer stones permit longer strokes, which I like. With the KME, you certainly can stroke the blade, but I find that scrubbing first and then stroking to smooth out any unevenness in the bevel is the best plan of action for this sharpener.

The only real issue I have about the KME's construction is that some of the adjustment knobs are rather small and my week fingers (due to a medical condition) make them difficult to operate. Of course, you may not have this problem if your hands have normal strength. I solved the problem quite easily, however. I just bought some larger knobs! (The threading is the ubiquitous 1/4-20.)

The basic KME kit comes in a hard plastic travel case and includes four diamond stones, labeled extra coarse (140 grit), coarse (300 grit), fine (600 grit) and extra fine (1500 grit). Note, however, that the base is not included in the kit. The kit price is $179.95 and the base is an additional $25. Alternatively, you can build your own base for a few dollars. (Strictly speaking, you can get by without the base, but I find it quite handy.)

Unfortunately, the extra-fine diamond stone will not give you a polished edge and there is a bit of a gap between it and a 0.5μ strop. As the KME web site puts it, the extra fine stone produces "true razor edges while retaining just a bit of a toothy bite." So if you want that smooth edge with a mirror polish, you will need to narrow this gap.

One option is to purchase some Chosera stones from KME. A 1000 and a 5000 Chosera should do the trick and will add about $75 to the price, bringing to total to about $255 sans base. If you are feeling flush, you can also add a 3000 and a 10000 stone to the kit. If you prefer the Shapton stones, they are available on a limited basis from Jende Industries but must be cut to order.

Alternatively, KME has just developed a series of diamond films that attach to glass plates of the same size as the diamond stones. These films should be available by the time you read these words and will come in a range of grit sizes to fill the gap between the extra fine diamond stone and a strop very nicely.

Wicked Edge

The **Wicked Edge sharpeners** (www.wickededgeusa.com) come in several flavors. There is a commercial model designed for high-volume sharpening as well as a field model designed for, well, the field.

The noncommercial, tabletop models come in three versions, named the *Generation I*, *Generation II* and *Generation 3 Pro*. (Yes, the model numbers apparently changed from Roman to Arabic.) The Generation I sharpener is available in a kit (details later) called the *Pro Pack I* and the Generation II sharpener is available in a kit (details later) called the *Pro Pack II*. The Generation 3 Pro is its own kit (details later).

The ProPack II is shown in Figure 109.

Figure 109: Wicked Edge Pro Pack II sharpening kit

The Generation 3 Pro is shown in Figure 110.

Figure 110: The new Generation 3 Pro model

All of the models are extremely well made, with solid, highly-refined precision parts.

Like the KME, the Wicked Edge systems use a clamp to hold the knife as well as a slidable arm to hold the stone at a constant angle to the knife. However, rather than clamping the knife with the blade parallel to the table, the Wicked Edge clamps the knife with the blade perpendicular to the table with the apex facing up and the handle pointed toward the sharpener. Moreover, there are *two* arms that each accommodate a stone of the same grit (two stones of each grit are supplied). Thus, you can swipe each side of the blade without changing the configuration of the machine. This is a very nice feature.

The stones for the Wicked Edge are two-sided, each side having a different (but clearly marked) level of abrasiveness. The company sells diamond stones from the very course (100) to the very fine (1000), along with even finer ceramic stones as well as kangaroo strops with diamond paste. They also sell curved stones for use in sharpening blades with a recurve. Both Shapton (Professional) and Chosera stones are available in the unique stone configuration of the Wicked Edge.

The Wicked Edge's clamp has the same potential drawback as the KME clamp (or any clamping system) and so there may be some knives that will not be held firmly by the clamp. In many cases, this problem can be overcome by taping or applying moleskin to the blade to change its configuration. Actually, taping is not be a bad idea in any case to protect the blade from being scratched.

The clamp that comes with the Generation I and Generation II models has one fixed, vertical jaw and one movable jaw. However, the company has developed an upgraded clamp kit in which both jaws move, which should provide secure clamping for more varieties of knife blades. The new clamp is standard on the Generation 3 Pro but is an upgrade for the earlier models.

It is also important to note that the newer clamp accommodates a maximum blade thickness of 3/16 inch, whereas the older clamp can accommodate blades with a thickness up to 1/4 inch. This may or may not be an issue for you—very few knives have blades that are thicker than 3/16 of an inch.

It might seem that alternating strokes on each side of the blade is the correct way to use this system and I have indeed seen many videos of sharpeners using precisely that procedure. The problem with taking only alternating strokes is that it is hard to tell when you are done with a given stone, unless you are willing to stop after *each* stroke to check for a burr! A more sensible approach is to take, say three to five (with a coarser stone) or five to ten (with a finer stone) swipes on one side of the blade, after which you can feel for a burr on the opposite side without having to change the configuration. You can repeat this procedure on each side of the blade until a burr appears. Then you can wear down the burr with alternating strokes. In this way, you minimize the size of the burr and also determine when to move to the next stone.

The Precision Sharpeners

The Generation I and Generation II sharpeners are referred to as *Precision Sharpeners* to distinguish them from the radically differently designed Generation 3 Pro model.

The Generation I sharpener has a bevel angle range of 15–30 degrees per side, whereas the Generation II model has upgraded hardware that provides an angle range of 13–35 degrees per side. The extra range will generally not be significant unless you sharpen knives with a steep chisel grid, for example.

The Pro Pack I kit comes with 100, 200, 400, 600, 800 and 1000 grit diamond stones, along with a leather stropping package containing 5μ and 3.5μ diamond paste. This may be all you will ever need, if you add a 0.5μ strop. The price is $425.

If you want to go all out, the Pro Pack II kit contains the same diamond stones along with two ceramic stones (1.4μ and 0.6μ) and two hones with 1.0μ and 0.5μ diamond paste. This model has an upgraded granite base and a digital angle gauge. It can also microadjust the angle by about 2 degrees, giving you the ability to set any sharpening angle. The price is $749.

The Generation 3 Pro

As you can see from the pictures, the design of this model is strikingly different from the other models, although the basic functionality is the same. Aside from the redesigned clamp that should accommodate more types of blades, the angle adjustment is entirely different. Instead of sliding the two arm brackets laterally to adjust the sharpening angle, the Generation 3 uses a lever in the front to set the angle of both arms simultaneously, which is simpler than the Allen wrench method of the earlier generation models. The angle range of this model is 14–26 degrees per side. There is also a microadjustment feature so that you can vary each arm individually by about 2°. Finally, there is a space provided to store the sharpening stones. The Generation 3 sells for $699, but you may want to supplement the stone set with a few ceramics because the sharpener comes with only the 100–1000 diamond stones.

Happenings

Clay Allison, the inventor of the Wicked Edge, tells me that there will be some changes coming in the near future. In particular, there will be some new sharpening systems available that work on the same two-arm principal as the current offerings. Also, some of the current offerings will be available with different options. Stay tuned to the Wicked Edge web site for further details.

 Work Sharp

The **Work Sharp Ken Onion Edition** (www.worksharptools.com) is essentially a small, variable speed belt sander with an adjustable angle guide. In case you cringe at the idea of sharpening a fine knife using as aggressive a tool as a belt sander, it happens that many large knife manufacturers as well as some custom knife makers use a *large* belt sander to sharpen their knives because they sharpen very quickly, so you are in good company here. (The belt sander is often followed by some additional work with stones or leather wheels.) Figure 111 shows the Work Sharp in action.

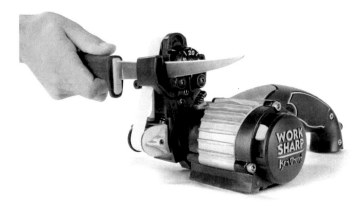

Figure 111: The Work Sharp Ken Onion Edition

You can also get a knife-grinding attachment, shown in Figure 112 that gives you more access to the belt. As you can see, the knife-grinding attachment does not have guides and can be used more easily with a freehand approach. The belts are also a bit wider, at 1 inch instead of 3/4 inch, which I find very helpful. Personally, I do all my Work Sharp sharpening with the knife-grinding attachment. There is a wide variety of different belts available for the Work Sharp, of various materials, grits and stiffnesses.

Figure 112: The knife grinding attachment

The price of the Work Sharp is $149 and the knife-grinding attachment is $99, but the street prices are less. Note that since the belt is not supported by a backing platen, it will flex and so the cutting bevel will have a *convex grind*.

The Work Sharp is a pleasure to use because it cuts very quickly and with minimal effort. Moreover, you can get a mirror polish on your cutting bevel with the finer belts. On the other hand, precisely because it does cut quickly, you need to be on your toes with this system. Also, the Work Sharp does not require lubricants, which is nice.

I like the Work Sharp a lot. In fact, I wish I had invented it! Being motorized, the Work Sharp provides quite a different sharpening experience from the other systems. When I need to sharpen quickly, this is the system I use. I basically just set the angle, insert a belt, turn on the machine and I am ready to sharpen. The other systems take a little more setup time.

However, when I feel like taking my time, listening to some Chopin, Mozart or Beethoven and trying to forget my troubles, I tend to pick one of the other systems. With stone-based systems, I can take that "one more gentle, ever-so-soft swipe" with the stone, for precision fine tuning, as it were. With the Work Sharp, the belt is moving so fast that "precision fine tuning" is quite a bit more challenging.

The Stone-Thickness Problem

All three of the assisted sharpening systems (KME, Edge Pro and Wicked Edge) suffer from a problem that I call the **stone-thickness problem**. This is the problem that when the stone thickness changes, so does the sharpening angle! This issue can be significant because, for example, diamond stones, which do not wear, are generally much thinner than ceramic stones, which are made thicker in order to compensate for wear. The difference in thickness can be as much as 1/4 of an inch in new stones, which could affect the angle by as much as a degree or so (depending on the geometry of the sharpener).

To explain this problem further, note that when the stone arm is directly over the clamp, all three systems essentially involve a triangle. Figure 113 shows a schematic of the Edge Pro Apex.

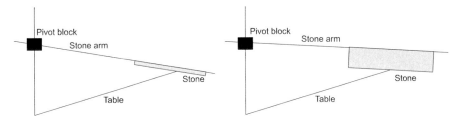

Figure 113: The stone-thickness problem

As you can see by comparing the two schematics in the figure, when you replace a thinner stone by a (somewhat exaggerated) thicker stone but do not move the pivot point, the angle that the stone arm makes with the table *decreases*. In other words, an *increase* in stone thickness *decreases* the sharpening angle, and vice versa.

Obviously, you must compensate for this change in sharpening angle. To do so, when you change stones, you just need to keep the stone arm *parallel* to its previous orientation. Put another way, putting in a thicker stone raises the stone arm at the blade end, so you must also raise the arm at the pivot block end to maintain the same arm orientation.

In fact, as shown on the left in Figure 114, all you need to do is raise (or lower) the pivot block by *roughly* the same amount as the *change in thickness* of the stone. So, for example, if the next stone in 3 mm. thicker, you need to raise the pivot by *approximately* 3 mm.

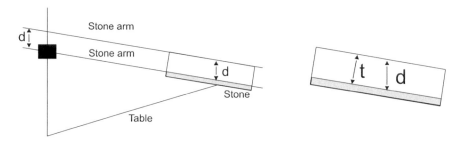

Figure 114: Stone-thickness compensation

I say "approximately" because the change t in thickness of the stone is a little smaller than the distance d that you need to move the arm to keep it at the same angle with the table. But as long as the stones are relatively thin, the *difference* between t and d is pretty small.

So, from a practical point of view, how do we keep the stone arm parallel for all stone thicknesses? On the Edge Pro Apex, the problem is neatly solved as shown in Figure 115.

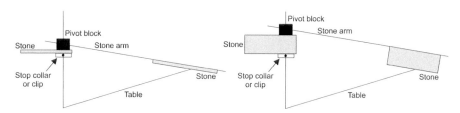

Figure 115: Solving the stone-thickness problem for the Apex

Here is the procedure. First, you will need to place a **stop collar** on the vertical arm of the Apex, as shown in Figure 115. A stop collar is just a steel ring with an Allen screw that can be tightened to keep the collar in place. These are used on drill bits to prevent the bit from going too deeply into the wood and should be available at most hardware stores. Alternatively, any clip that can be fastened *tightly* to the vertical arm will do.

Next, decide which stone you want to use to set the sharpening angle (probably using the Sharpie trick). Set the sharpening angle with that stone. By the way, I often use a much finer stone to set the angle than the one I intend to start the sharpening with because if I my initial sharpening angle guess is too high, I don't want the stone to roll over the edge of the knife too much.

Once you have set the sharpening angle with a reference stone, remove it from the stone arm and place it underneath the pivot block. Then snug the stop collar directly underneath the stone, as shown on the left in Figure 115. *In this way, you have set the top of the stop collar to the correct location for the bottom of the pivot block when there is no stone in the stone arm.* The top of the stop collar is now the correct reference point for all stones, regardless of their thickness! Pretty neat, huh?

So, for each subsequent stone, before clamping it into the stone arm, simply place it on top of the stop collar and adjust the pivot block so that it rests on the stone.

For the Wicked Edge, a stop collar will not work. However, you can purchase an optional accessory called the Variable Stone Thickness Adapter for $40 that will allow you to perform the analog of the stop collar trick on this system.

On the KME sharpening system, the parts seem a bit too small for a physical clamp, so adjusting for various stone thicknesses will require some ingenuity. Of course, you can always use the Sharpie trick to reset the angle when the stone thickness changes.

The Even-Bevel Issue

Another issue that will arise with assisted sharpeners is that the sharpening angle will generally change as the stone arm swings away from dead center, especially towards the tip of the blade. If the apex of the blade is a straight line as in a sheepsfoot knife or a portion of a true circle (very unlikely), then the sharpening angle remains constant throughout the blade, but these are the only normal cases in which the angle does not change.

An Explanation

If you are interested in an explanation, read on, but I will need to remind you of two simple geometric facts. First, recall that given a straight line and a point that is not on that line, there is *exactly one* plane containing both the line and the point, as shown in Figure 116.

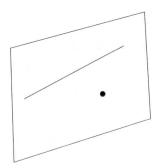

Figure 116: Exactly one plane containing a line and a point

Second, recall that every point on a curve has a *tangent line*, as shown in Figure 117.

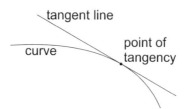

Figure 117: The tangent line to a curve at a point

That's all the geometry we need.

Now, Figure 118 describes the whole situation for the Wicked Edge sharpener. The same idea applies to the KME and the Edge Pro.

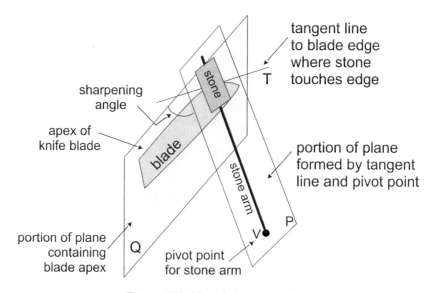

Figure 118: The whole story is here

Let us look at the parts in this figure. First note the shaded plane Q, which is the plane containing the apex of the blade to be sharpened. Next, note the stone arm with a stone attached and note the arm's pivot point V. Now, imagine that you are sharpening this blade and suddenly stop moving the stone arm, with the stone resting on the apex of the blade.

In theory at least, the stone is touching the apex of the blade at only one point. Moreover, the plane P containing the stone also contains the *tangent line* T to the blade at that point of contact. Therefore, the plane P is the unique plane containing the tangent line T and the pivot point V of the stone arm.

The reason I went through all of this (which I hope was not too stressful) is that the sharpening angle is just the angle between the two planes P and Q!

Now, the question (and the whole point of this discussion) is whether or not that angle changes as you move the stone along the apex of the blade.

To answer this question, suppose first that the apex is a straight line, as it would be for a sheepsfoot blade. Then the answer is that the angle does not change. The reason is simple: A straight line (the blade apex) has the property that at every point on that line, the tangent line is actually the line itself and so the tangent line does not change as we move along the apex of the blade. Therefore, the plane P is the same plane no matter where the stone is touching the blade. Since the plane Q containing the blade certainly never changes, the sharpening angle never changes.

If the apex of the blade is not a straight line, things become significantly more complicated. First, we can say that if the tangent line is different at two points on the blade, then the corresponding planes P will also be different.

This follows from the simple fact that the intersection of the planes P and Q is the tangent line T. After all, the intersection of two nonparallel planes is a line and T is the *only* line that lies in both planes. So, suppose that T_1 and T_2 are two *different* tangent lines, corresponding to two different positions of the stone on the blade. Both of these tangent lines lie in the plane Q, of course. Suppose that P_1 and P_2 are the planes made by these two tangent lines and the pivot point. Then as we have just discussed, the intersection of P_1 and Q is T_1 and the intersection of P_2 and Q is T_2, so if P_1 and P_2 were the *same* plane, then T_1 and T_2 would have to be the *same* line, which we are assuming is not the case. So the plane P changes as we move the stone along the blade.

However, just because P changes does not necessarily mean that the *angle* between P and Q must change! In fact, as shown in Figure 119, for a circular blade, if you clamp the knife so that the pivot point is directly in front of the center of the circle, then it seems pretty obvious on the grounds of symmetry that the sharpening angle will remain constant. This can be proven mathematically, but I assume you would prefer me to skip the details.

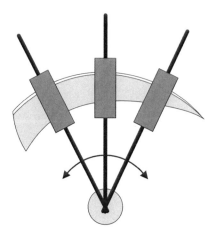

Figure 119: A circular blade

It is also possible to prove mathematically that the only two blade types for which the sharpening angle remains constant are the straight (sheepsfoot) blade and a circular blade. However, the proof actually involves some rather sophisticated mathematics (nonlinear differential equations) and so I will spare you the details.

Conclusion

For sheepsfoot blades and circular blades, the sharpening angle remains constant as you swing the stone arm. However, in general, for the curved blades encountered in real life, the sharpening angle will change as the stone moves along the curved portion of the blade. Thus, you will encounter an effect similar to the (highly exaggerated) one shown in Figure 120.

Figure 120: Uneven bevel

For short blades or for fairly straight blades, the effect is minor. However, this is something that you should take into account when you position the knife in the clamp. Of course, with the Edge Pro, you can slide the knife horizontally to mitigate this issue if necessary.

 # Stropping

In the knife world, **stropping** refers to rubbing the blade over a relatively soft *stropping medium* such as leather (cow, horse or kangaroo), nano cloth (explained later) or even balsa wood that has been impregnated with a *polishing compound*.

Bear in mind that with an ultra-polishing stone, you can rub the bevel of the knife both forward and backward. However, *pushing* the blade along a piece of leather will simply cause the knife edge to dig into the leather, ruining the strop. Instead, you always pull the knife *away* from the cutting edge.

There is some difference of opinion as to whether stopping should be done at the same angle as sharpening or at a slightly higher angle. There is also some debate as to the amount of pressure one should use in stropping, although I think that most people favor *light to very light* pressure. The danger in incorrect stropping is that you might roll over the delicate edge that you have painstakingly created during the refinement process. All this is something you will need to decide for yourself after some experimentation.

 ## Polishing Compounds

There are many types of **polishing compounds**, also known as **honing compounds** or **lapping compounds**. Here are the major types.

1) Until recently, the most common form of stropping compound was an abrasive powder, such as chromium oxide or aluminum oxide embedded in a wax-like base with the consistency of a soft crayon. These compounds come in a variety of grits that are usually distinguished by color: white, green, brown, yellow and so on.
2) **Diamond paste** is also available in various particle sizes, such as 6μ, 3μ and 1μ.
3) The latest types of stropping compounds are the ultra-fine **diamond emulsions** (0.1μ, 0.05μ and 0.025μ) and the less expensive **boron carbide emulsions** (0.5μ–8μ) and the even less expensive **aluminum oxide emulsions** (1μ, 0.3μ and 0.05μ). These are made by Ken Schwartz (and possibly others).

Thus, stropping does overlap polishing with the finest ceramic stones. However, the lower limit of stone-based polishing is at about 0.5μ, which is generally where most stropping begins, so I will limit my discussion to stropping at 0.5μ or below.

 ## Stropping Media

There are also several options for stropping media. The traditional medium is cow leather, generally smooth, fine-grained and firm. This material makes a perfect strop for practical sharpening. And of course, an old purse can make a decent stropping medium and it is free. (You will still need to buy a polishing compound.)

However, many experts say that **horse butt** is better than cow hide because it has a tighter grain structure and less fat (but I suppose that depends on the horse?). If you can't bring yourself to get behind a horse butt, there is also **kangaroo**, which is very smooth and flat. (I could say: "If you really want to use kangaroo, hop to it," but I won't.)

Another option is **nano cloth**, which is an extremely fine and consistently woven cloth, whose exact composition is apparently proprietary. Kangaroo leather is much firmer and slicker than the nano cloth, which has a definite bite. Figure 121 shows a kangaroo strop with a 0.1μ diamond emulsion. Note how the abrasive particles appear to settle in the pores of the leather.

Figure 121: Kangaroo with 0.1μ diamond emulsion (30x)

Figure 122 shows a nano cloth strop with the same 0.1μ diamond emulsion. Note how the emulsion seems to spread throughout the tightly woven cloth.

Figure 122: Nano cloth with 0.1μ diamond emulsion (30x)

I have used both kangaroo and nano cloth and like them both. This choice again comes down to personal preference.

 *Why Strop?*

Regardless of whether you are freehand sharpening or using an assisted or motorized sharpening system, you will want to end your sharpening with a strop. My experience tells me that stropping definitely does improve the sharpness of a blade. Of course, *this is assuming that the blade was properly refined before stropping.* You can't strop a piece of concrete!

Equally important is the fact that frequent stropping *between sharpenings* is the best way to prolong the sharpness of a blade and delay the sharpening process as long as possible. When I begin to detect that my knife is getting a bit less sharp than a moment ago, I grab the strop.

The KME, Edge Pro and Wicket Edge systems have leather or tape "stones" with which you can strop at a consistent angle. The Work Sharp has honing belts that come close to stropping. Personally, I prefer to strop freehand, since no setup is involved and I can strop much more easily between sharpenings. In fact, I keep a couple of strops with 0.5μ compound around my woodworking shop so I can reach them at a moment's notice. I also keep one near my knife collection.

Nano-Stropping

Given that stropping at 0.5μ is very helpful, the question naturally arises as to whether **nano-stropping**, that is, stropping below 0.5μ is also helpful.

You will be happy to hear that I took the bullet for you and bought some extreme stropping materials, namely, kangaroo and nano cloth strops and diamond emulsions at 0.1μ, 0.050μ and 0.025μ. (I hated to do it, but I owe it to my readers.) Here are my conclusions.

To be perfectly frank, I often but not always notice a *very subtle* increase in sharpness after stropping with 0.1μ nano-gunk. However, I do not notice any real difference with the finer emulsions. Perhaps I would notice more of a difference were I sharpening straight razors, but I have had a full beard for over 45 years, so the issue has not come up lately.

To Nano-Strop or Not To Nano-Strop, That Is The Question

On the question of whether or not to nano-strop, we must separate practice from theory. I believe that nano-stropping has no place in practical sharpening. The main problem is that the effects of nano-stropping are fleeting at best. What's the point of spending the time and money to get an edge that will disappear with your first cut?

On the other hand, for theoretical sharpening, the goal is to obtain the sharpest possible edge, regardless of its longevity. I believe that nano-stropping can improve the sharpness of the edge, *provided that it is done correctly.* The problem is that poor stropping technique (at any level) can *easily* make the edge duller than it was before stropping. Keep in mind that the best technique for nano-stropping (or any stropping) will depend on the stropping medium and will be different for kangaroo leather than for nano cloth, for example.

My "problem" with nano-stropping is that I can get a hair-whittling edge without nano-stropping and I am quite content to stop at hair-whittling sharpness. (Figure 87 was a result of stropping at 0.5μ only.) As a consequence, I can only recommend spending the extra money on nano-stropping equipment if you really want to try to push the envelope. However, you are going to need a test of sharpness that goes beyond hair-whittling. If you find such a test, please drop me an email.

In summary, for practical sharpening, I finish with the 0.5μ strop. For theoretical sharpening, I do nano-strop at all levels but am still looking for a technique that will give me a more consistent and more noticeable improvement in sharpness. If I don't find one before my nano-gunk runs out (which will take quite some time), I will probably not buy it again.

Stropping Without Compound

I have heard some sharpening "experts" suggest stropping on bare leather, with no added compound. I have heard others say that this is not effective. Of course, you can easily to check for yourself whether or not this works for you. I am quite happy with the results of stropping with a compound, so I have not done any significant testing in this regard.

However, here is what Professor Verhoeven (a metallurgist) says in his paper *Experiments on Knife Sharpening* on the subject of stropping with and without a stropping compound. The waterstone sharpening he refers to was done with either a 6000 or an 8000 grit waterstone (it didn't seem to make any difference).

> Stropping of the waterstone sharpened blades on clean leather strops had little effect upon the geometry of the as-sharpened blades. The abrasive grooves on faces and the burr size along the edge were not significantly modified. [...] Apparently, the natural abrasives in clean leather, on either the hard or soft side of the leather, is not adequate to produce a significant abrasion of the surface.

> Stropping of the waterstone sharpened blades on a leather strop loaded with [0.5 micron] chrome oxide compound produced a significant change in the edge geometry of the blades. The abrasive grooves from the waterstone sharpening were smoothed out significantly. The edge burr width was not reduced significantly below the 0.5 micron level of the waterstone ground blades, but it was perhaps a bit more uniform along the edge. However, the burs on 600 grit pre-sharpened blades were reduced significantly, to the same level as on the pre-sharpened waterstone blades. The overall

geometry of the stropped edges compared favorably to the razor blade standards.

 # My Recommendations

I hope that my discussion of sharpening methods has been of some help to you. I know that there are a bewildering number of choices and that the decision of which direction to go is not easy. Let me make a few comments that reflect my opinion only but perhaps will be of some help in making your decision.

Strop Blocks

First, I want to mention that I am partial to a pre-fabricated stropping product called a **Strop Block** from knivesplus.com. This is a piece of MDF to which a piece of leather has been attached. The leather is carefully and painstakingly endowed with a chromium oxide abrasive that the company says has about a 0.5 micron particle size. Each strop block is tested before it is shipped and you can see from the block itself that much care has been taken in its preparation.

Troney Toler, the developer of the Strop Block told me that it took over 10 years to perfect the strop. According to Troney, the key to a successful product is in choosing the right leather, which needs to have just the right amount of nap: The leather must not be too smooth nor too rough. He also tells me that the strop is so forgiving that the precise stropping angle is immaterial! (I will let you judge that for yourself.) He says that the strop block should last many years and needs no maintenance. The price is $20. I own several and use them often.

Freehand Sharpening

I have already expressed my opinions about freehand sharpening. To reiterate, I generally prefer diamond stones, followed by a Spyderco ultra fine ceramic, followed by a strop.

If you decide to learn freehand sharpening, then I have a couple of suggestions, although these are probably not the only routes you can take. First, I would be very careful when it comes to buying diamond stones. Poor quality diamond stones are simply a waste of money, so be careful when making your choice.

One possibility is to buy two DMT DiaSharp (or similar quality) diamond stones along with a Spyderco ceramic, either the 2x8 inch or the 3x8 inch stone. Make sure you can return the Spyderco stone if you decide that it is not flat enough. Amazon prices currently are $51 for the coarse DMT, $59 for the extra fine DMT, $42 for the 2x8 Spyderco and $85 for the 3x8 Spyderco. This brings the total to either $153 or $195. Note that this is a completely unguided system, so you should expect that it will take some (perhaps considerable) practice before you become proficient at using this system.

Alternatively, you could purchase a Work Sharp Guided Sharpening System along with the upgrade kit. I think this will provide a quicker road to a successful result. The combined price for these tools is about $95.

In both cases, you will want to buy a strop.

Sharpening Systems

I wish I could say that one of the assisted sharpening systems stands clearly above the others, but in my mind this is not the case. All of the systems that I have discussed are excellent in their own way, so I do not think you can make a bad choice.

Just to satisfy myself, I recently purchased five identical knives in the $20 price range and sharpened one knife each using the Work Sharp, the Edge Pro, the KME and the Wicked Edge systems. I sharpened the fifth knife freehand. All of the knives came out razor-sharp and so I can say categorically that *every one of these sharpening systems can work exceptionally well*. Therefore, the difference really does come down to personal preference.

Although the following may not be of much help to you, I can say that if I had to choose exactly *two* systems, one would be the Work Sharp. When I need a quick sharpening, I use the Work Sharp. I generally use the Work Sharp for my work-horse type folders that need sharpening quite a bit more often than my gentleman's folders. Also, I like to use it for my kitchen knives when stropping doesn't do the job, because I usually discover that a kitchen knife is not performing up to my satisfaction while I am in the initial "cutting-up" stage of preparing a meal and I don't want to spend a lot of time sharpening.

The price I pay for the extra speed is that I lose some measure of *fine* control over the edge. With the other sharpening systems, I can take a few final ever-so-gentle "wisps" of the stone over the blade. I find wisping a little difficult to do on a belt sander, but perhaps that is *my* shortcoming.

As to the other sharpeners, as I said, they are all quite good. If your decision is driven largely by budget considerations, note that the Edge Pro Apex will run about $300 (with the flattening kit) and the KME about $280, both without a strop. The Wicked Edge is considerably more expensive, ranging from $425 to $749 depending on the model, and you may still want to supplement the system with some additional stones. (However, as I mentioned earlier, things are reportedly changing at Wicked Edge, so these prices may change as well.)

If you have some budget flexibility, I suppose the next decision you need to make is whether you prefer a clamp-based design (KME or Wicked Edge) or not (Edge Pro). If not, the Edge Pro is your choice by process of elimination. If so, you still have a choice. If portability is a priority, the KME has a definite advantage. Also, it is easier to watch the edge develop on the KME than on the Wicked Edge, due to the orientations of the knife when it is clamped in place. But if you really like the idea of a rock-solid system and the ability to rapidly alternate strokes on both sides of the blade, the Wicked Edge has the advantage.

Since my role here is to give you options, here is one more that I feel compelled to mention. If you lean towards the Edge Pro-style system but your budget is tight, there are several "clone" versions of this system on Amazon that sell for about $30! I have not tried any of these clones, but the reviews on Amazon and the videos on YouTube are definitely encouraging. I gather that the main problem with these clones is the stones. However, reviewers indicate that the authentic Edge Pro stones fit these clone systems! Also, you may need to make a few modifications to the clone, because as you would expect, quality control is not too good on these systems. Nevertheless, one of these clones, along with a set of original Edge Pro stones and a flattening kit will run you about half the cost of an Edge Pro kit, enough savings to buy a pretty nice folder.

 # Edge Maintenance

OK, so now you know all about sharpening and can produce the perfect edge. How do you maintain this edge as long as possible?

Here is what I do. As soon as I begin to sense that my knife has lost a bit more performance than I want, I strop. I keep a stropping block handy and strop *often*. Stropping will help maintain the edge as long as possible. Remember: technique is very important when stropping because it is easy to round over the edge and make it worse. Light pressure is generally better.

When stropping does not restore the edge, I sometimes try to quickly refine the edge with the stone I generally use last in my complete sharpening routine. Then I strop again. If the blade is not too dull, this will bring it back to razor sharpness.

However, when this doesn't do the trick, it's time to do a proper refining. Climbing up the grit ladder one stone at a time wastes both time and stone, so based on my experience, I pick a stone that I think is the proper place to start the refining process. I seldom need to start with the same stone I used when I first sharpened the knife, because the edge is still in much better shape than when it came from the factory and no reprofiling is necessary.

Good luck and thanks for reading!

Index